PREDICTING AND CONTROLLING DISEASE

PUBLIC HEALTH IN THE 21ST CENTURY

Additional books in this series can be found on Nova's website under the Series tab.

Additional e-books in this series can be found on Nova's website under the e-book tab.

PREDICTING AND CONTROLLING DISEASE

MARCUS HUTBER

Nova Biomedical

New York

NOTICE TO THE READER

The Publisher has taken reasonable care in the preparation of this book, but makes no expressed or implied warranty of any kind and assumes no responsibility for any errors or omissions. No liability is assumed for incidental or consequential damages in connection with or arising out of information contained in this book. The Publisher shall not be liable for any special, consequential, or exemplary damages resulting, in whole or in part, from the readers' use of, or reliance upon, this material. Any parts of this book based on government reports are so indicated and copyright is claimed for those parts to the extent applicable to compilations of such works.

Independent verification should be sought for any data, advice or recommendations contained in this book. In addition, no responsibility is assumed by the publisher for any injury and/or damage to persons or property arising from any methods, products, instructions, ideas or otherwise contained in this publication.

This publication is designed to provide accurate and authoritative information with regard to the subject matter covered herein. It is sold with the clear understanding that the Publisher is not engaged in rendering legal or any other professional services. If legal or any other expert assistance is required, the services of a competent person should be sought. FROM A DECLARATION OF PARTICIPANTS JOINTLY ADOPTED BY A COMMITTEE OF THE AMERICAN BAR ASSOCIATION AND A COMMITTEE OF PUBLISHERS.

Additional color graphics may be available in the e-book version of this book.

LIBRARY OF CONGRESS CATALOGING-IN-PUBLICATION DATA

ISBN: 978-1-63463-029-0
Library of Congress Control Number: 2014950566

Published by Nova Science Publishers, Inc. † New York

CONTENTS

Preface

This book has primarily been aimed at epidemiologists working with empirical data for both human and veterinary diseases. The final paragraph of this preface is probably the most important paragraph of the book, and if epidemiologists or healthcare or veterinary administrators are converted to the concept outlined in the last paragraph, then the book will have served a useful purpose: twenty-five years of epidemiological research have culminated in the concept described in the paragraph.

Historically, mathematics was introduced to epidemiology in the 1980s to provide a methodology for forecasting epidemic outcomes or scenarios. Those outcomes or scenarios were seen as an accurate way of predicting the future in terms of disease epidemiology, and were gradually accepted by administrators as a reliable tool for controlling infectious diseases. Whilst the idea was excellent in theory, there was subsequently a string of prominent and public failures of these mathematical models to predict and control disease. The failures of mathematical models culminated in the mistakes of the 2001 UK foot-and-mouth disease epidemic where 83% of the individuals slaughtered were disease-free and thus were culled unnecessarily. The culling had been highlighted by modellers as a necessary measure for disease control, but at the precise moment that prominent modellers had made the call for extensive animal slaughter, the disease was later shown to have been held under control.

Consequently, epidemiologists within the veterinary industry differed from mathematical modellers in their approach to subsequent disease control for the future. Whilst the modellers preferred an approach that implemented extensive control (to thin the susceptible population and to minimise the level of infectious individuals), veterinary epidemiologists preferred a more targeted approach: veterinarians deemed that excessive overkill of livestock was unnecessary and in 2001 the English populace agreed with them. These differences are discussed in this book since they have generated a series of debates within the literature. Ultimately, veterinary epidemiologists became suspicious of algorithms that were occultly concealed within 'black box' mathematical jargon, whilst mathematical modellers began to view the veterinary epidemiologists as laggards in terms of cutting-edge science. This book examines both the methodologies of conventional maths modelling and the essential epidemiology that enables biomaths models to be formulated. Some of the important concepts are deliberately repeated and re-explained. New methodologies are introduced (APRISM, vector-transition, economic equations, spatial model components, etc.) and these demonstrate that first generation mathematical modelling is continually adapting or evolving as more diseases are modelled with disparate characteristics. The failing of first generation models to accurately predict disease prevalence (or the duration of epidemics or their traceable course) is correlated with the level of estimates that are required for various model components. The number of model components (or factors) that are estimated is positively correlated with the degree of inaccuracy exhibited in simulated epidemic scenarios. First generation maths models all share the same problem with multiply estimated biological factors [such as R_0, or incubation period, or infectious period, or effective contact rate, etc.]. Multiple estimates will cumulatively compound the overall level of model inaccuracy.

This book introduces second generation epidemiological modelling. Second generation modelling uses directly measurable biofactors that do not require estimates for their quantitative values. Biomodels encompass multiple model factors that would otherwise have to be estimated, and as such biofactors are directly correlated with disease prevalence and epidemic duration. This correlation enables biomodels to accurately predict the future course of an epidemic before it unfolds, whilst concurrently directing healthcare administrators where to target manpower and financial resources for optimal disease control. Whereas first generation modelling remains a useful tool for pedagogical or teaching purposes, second generation modelling [in the form of biomodels] allows healthcare administrators to cope with the demands of immediate and rapid disease control during periods of disease epidemics. Biomodels should be developed for important infectious diseases during periods of epidemiological 'peacetime', when manpower and resources are not held at a premium.

Few non-fictional books are read cover-to-cover. To accommodate the selective reader, some of the most important concepts in this volume [such as biofactors, biomodels, subclinical disease and predictive accuracy] are repeated within relevant chapters.

National and regional disease contingency planning should incorporate biomodels as useful tools when planning future disease control measures.

Dr. Marcus Hutber
PetCare Limited, Director
78 Wesley Road, Winchester
Hampshire, England S0323 7PX
Tel: 0044-7814-526409
hutber@epivet.co.uk

Glossary

The following definitions are not generic but relate specifically to this book:

Absorbing state   A disease state into which individuals enter but do not exit.

Agonistic   Aggressive or confrontational behaviour arising between individuals within a population.

Age group   A group of individuals whose ages from birth fall within a pre-defined range.

APRISM   Class of epidemiological model placing individuals into one of six distinct disease states: affected, partially-immune, recovered, immune, susceptible or mildly-affected.

Biofactor   An epidemiological factor that is accurately correlated with a desired model output and is used predictively.

Biomodel   An epidemiological model that utilises biofactors for predictive simulations.

Bottom-up solutions   Complex models with components that represent many facets of a modelled system.

CHP   Calf hardening pen.

CIP   Critical inter-vaccination period, or the temporal interval between two regular prophylactic vaccine-tion programmes, beyond (or exceeding) which vaccinal protection for individuals begins to drop below the immunity threshold.

CR	Contact rate, quantifying the number of contacts between one infected individual and susceptible individuals within a population.
DE	Differential equation, describing rates of entry and exit of individuals from disease states within a model.
DR	Disease ratio of measured acute disease to quantified subclinical disease for any given disease.
Deterministic	The average of many repeated outcomes involving the element of chance.
ECR	Effective contact rate, quantifying the number of disease transmitting contacts between an infected individual and susceptible individuals within a population.
EpiMan	Software devised to model, monitor and facilitate control of FMD in New Zealand.
FDI	First day incidence, or the number of newly affected individuals on day 1 of an outbreak.
FMD	Foot-and-mouth disease.
FMDV	Foot-and-mouth disease virus.
Fomite	Inanimate source carrying infection.
Group age	The length of time that an individual has remained within its current disease group.
Host	Individuals within a population that carry clinical or subclinical infection.
IAHP	Institute for Animal Health, or the Pirbright Institute.
IMP	Immeasurable model parameter representing one or more components of a modelled system.
INCB	Incubation period.
Incidence	The number of newly infected individuals or measured units (such as IPs) for any given time interval during an outbreak or epidemic.
IP	Infected premises.
ITOES	Period from infection to the end of clinical signs.
MDA	Maternally-derived antibody gained following parturition.
Micropopulation	A disease in which the parasite multiplies prolifically within the host. The host population can be divided into a few disease classes, creating a compartmental model.

PcPv	Pre-challenge post-vaccination.
PcPv period	Period from the final pre-challenge vaccination to day 1 of a successful challenge against a herd.
Population Matrix	A two dimensional array recording disease status and other details of population matrix individuals.
PoPv	Pre-outbreak post-vaccination.
PoPv period	Period from the final pre-outbreak vaccination to day 1 of an outbreak.
POV	Post-outbreak vaccination.
POV day	Post-outbreak day of administration of vaccine.
Prevalence	The number of infected individuals in a population/population size, or population % infected, for a given time interval.
Probability matrix	A two dimensional array holding the probabilitiesof one individual transferring between any two disease states.
Prophylactic	A measure to prevent infection within apopulation.
SDI	Second day incidence, or the number of newly infected individuals on day 2 of an outbreak.
SIR	Class of simple epidemiological model representing three disease states: susceptible, infected and recovered.
State-transition	Modelling method that moves individuals between pre-defined states of a disease.
State vectors	The population sizes of each disease state, at the start or end of a time interval during a simulation.
Stochastic	Outcomes which are determined partly by chance even when the initial conditions are constant.
Subclinical	Infected and usually infectious, but not exhibiting disease signs.
TCID	Tissue culture infective dose, where $TCID_{50}$ [also termed TCID50] becomes the TCID required to kill 50% of infected cells.
Top-down solutions	Simple models that only include components shown to significantly affect model output.
Vector-transition	Modelling method that moves herd animals between vectors, where each vector represents several states of a disease.

Section A: Predicting Disease Spread

This section (incorporating chapters 1 & 2) examines disease modelling, focusing upon the inaccurate and accurate predictions for rate, prevalence and extent of disease spread, and evaluating both the academically theoretical and the implementable or practicable.

Methodologies that are outlined in this section take disease modelling into a second generation. Second generation models (or biomodels) confer a significantly increased level of accuracy in predictive disease simulation: biomodels monitor the complex biology of disease spread, rather than simplifying the biology in order to accommodate the necessary modelling mathematics.

Whilst biomodels allow epidemiologists to accurately predict both prevalence and durations of epidemics and outbreaks, those predictions are available for disease control administrators at the diagnosis of initial clinical signs; moreover, the way in which biomodels work are transparent for administrators and not occultly hidden as 'black box' components within complex algorithms. Furthermore, biomodels outline the appropriate course of action for optimal disease control during an epidemic or outbreak.

Chapter 1

Predicting the Future with Epidemiological Models

1.1. Introduction

The advent of computers has enabled complex systems to be analysed and simulated in real time, to the extent that computer-based maths models of disease spread can currently forecast the likely progress of an outbreak (at the local level) or epidemic (at the regional or national level). The question that arises however, is how likely is the forecasted disease spread? If a maths model is synonymous with the biology of the disease then the model simulations will be very likely, and therefore accurate in detailing how the disease will spread. Nevertheless, since the biology of any given disease is always complex, then the accuracy of a maths model is dependent upon the identification of the most important model components (or modelling factors), descending down to the least important modelling factors. The process of prioritising the respective modelling factors through a systems analysis is described in this section.

This chapter examines first generation epidemiological maths modelling, its methodologies and its relative successes and failures. Whilst there are a number of different techniques that have been employed in the literature to model disease spread, the more accurate methodologies are discussed in this chapter. Less accurate methodologies become less interesting per se. New methodologies are introduced (APRISM, vector-transition, economic equations, spatial model components, etc.) and these are discussed in detail.

1.2. Creating a Disease Model

An epidemiological model enables simulations of disease spread to be run at the local level (as an outbreak) or at the national/regional level (as an epidemic). Each simulation run is biologically equivalent to a film recording of the course of the disease: snapshots of disease events (equivalent to photographs) are presented at regular time periods (creating a film), but the represented time periods are significantly shortened, so that the simulation effectively becomes a speeded up version of events. Graphically, the simulations are very appealing for administrators and epidemiologists alike. However, the danger of visually appealing graphics is that they can convey an impression of an epidemiological accuracy that may or may not be justified. For first generation mathematical modelling the epidemiological reality was that the conveyed accuracy was more often unjustified.

The snapshots that are taken to create the epidemiological model simulations are an analysis of different states or forms of a disease that hosts (humans or individuals) can exhibit. For example, the most simplistic model described by Anderson and May (1991) places all individuals from a population into just three disease states. Namely, susceptible [where individuals are capable of becoming infected but have not yet contracted the disease], infected [where individuals have contracted the disease and may or may not yet be exhibiting clinical signs] and recovered [where individuals have contracted the disease and have exhibited clinical signs but may or may not still be infectious to other individuals].

Each snapshot at time period t [where t has a value from zero to n, and n can be specified as an input value for the model in the form of an integer] analyses how many individuals from a population are likely to be found within each of the disease states. The output of a model lists the calculated numbers of individuals in each of the disease states, and clearly those numbers will change as individuals move between the respective disease states.

The key disease state(s) for disease control administrators are the infected (also known as affected) and mildly-affected states, since these states give a quantitative value for disease incidence and disease prevalence. Disease incidence is taken to be the number of individuals that have moved into the infected (ie. affected) disease states during any given time period t_n and disease prevalence is taken to be the number of individuals that are in the infected (ie. affected) disease states at the end of any given time period t_n [divided by the population size]. Disease spread is taken to be under control once the level of incidence has reached a peak and has begun to decrease. The impact of an epidemic or outbreak [at any given time period] is measured by disease prevalence, since prevalence is expressed as a percentage of the total population, and therefore indicates how widespread the disease has become within that population. The number of individuals within the recovered state of a model becomes important at the end of an epidemic or outbreak, since it indicates the overall effect of the disease upon the population throughout its course [equivalent to the cumulative prevalence]: so long as recovered individuals remain immune (and therefore do not re-enter the susceptible state) and there are also few fatalities, then the number of recovereds can be divided by the population size. The resultant figure will be the percentage of the population that became infected during the course of the epidemic or outbreak. At time t_0 [where t_0 indicates the start of the first time period] the number of individuals falling within the susceptible disease state [or group] can be divided by the population size, giving the susceptibility of a population to a disease.

Hence, susceptibility, incidence, prevalence and final infected% [of the population] are all useful measures for epidemiologists to gauge the spread of a given disease through a population.

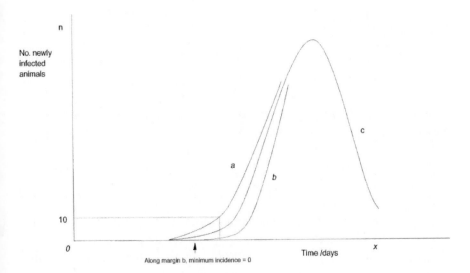

Figure 1. Simulation of an intra-herd FMD outbreak, showing modelled stochastic margins around the incidence curve.

Where a disease causes a high number of fatalities, then the SIR model fails, in that an additional disease state (for deceased individuals) is consequently required. Further changes to the model components will invariably be required for different diseases, and every model will require a tailoring of the disease states [or groups] to fit the epidemiological characteristics for any given disease. A selection of these tailoring processes is discussed below.

1.3. Initial Approach via a Stochastic APRISM Simulation Model

A stochastic component to a model is frequently desired to cater for the role of chance that is characteristic of epidemiological simulations: in the words of Abbey (1976) 'An epidemic is not uniquely determined by the initial conditions because at each period there are variations due to chance.' Hence, multiple runs from simulation models provide the stochastic margins to a deterministic outcome (Figure 1), where a deterministic outcome does not cater for the impact of chance variations. Monte-Carlo stochasticism (Robinson et al., 1993) was applied by James and Rossiter (1989) to their model of rinderpest. They reserved stochasticism for model components that were affected by chance. Thus, it was not applied to the latter stages of an outbreak, since small fluctuations (from the deterministic incidence) would have little effect upon disease persistence. However, it did become an integral factor in the early establishment of the disease, because of the plausibility of fade-out (Anderson and May, 1985). The James-Rossiter model for Rinderpest (1989) is an interesting framework around which to construct an initial model of an infectious disease, in that it affords both immediate applicability as well as adaptability for the micropopulation diseases [that include viral and bacterial infectious agents].

There is an inclusion of three additional disease groups (partially-immune, immune and mildly-affected) above and beyond the Anderson and May (1985) SIR model framework, creating an APRISM model with Affected, Partially-immune, Recovered, Immune, Susceptible and Mildly-affected disease states. This framework is capable of modelling varying levels of antibody protection for viral and some bacterial diseases (Figure 2). Antibody titres are likely to form a high proportion of incidence variation for outbreaks and epidemics of infectious diseases, and will therefore play an important component role within models at the local level (detailing outbreaks) as well as at the regional level (detailing epidemics). The affected group in Figure 2 includes both infectious individuals and those only incubating the disease. By monitoring group age [or the time spent by individuals within a group or disease state] a distinction can be made between infected individuals that are excreting the disease agent [virus or bacteria] and those that are not – group age specifically determines whether an individual is infectious. Thus, there is no disease group for 'infected but not infectious' individuals (or incubators) and this keeps the model less complex or less processor intensive.

1.3.1. Contact Spread

A noteworthy characteristic of the James-Rossiter approach is the modelling of disease through contact spread. Whereas the epidemiology of regional spread is often dependent upon various factors (including the movement of infected individuals, infected foodstuffs, aerosol transmission, fomites and persistently infected carrier individuals of the agent: Rweyemamu et al., 1982) local disease spread is governed by close individual contact, and is thereby suited to the James-Rossiter structure. Counter-intuitively, a modified version of contact spread has been shown to be applicable at the regional level (Hutber et al., 2005) and this is particularly relevant where environmental humidity < 60%. Hence, the model structure and the parameters outlined by Rossiter and James (1989) fit the requirements suggested above, for both local and regional spread models. Specifically, these model components [or parameters] epidemiologically accommodate population segregations, a vaccinal programme, and directly measurable model parameters such as effective contact rate (ECR). ECR is a mathematical model component that is specific to first generation maths epidemiological models. R_0 [or reproductive rate] is an equivalent component used by modellers who favour differential equations rather than probability matrices.

Key concept 1: **Most first generation mathematical models cannot directly measure ECR or R_0, and are therefore littered with modelling assumptions and estimated weighting factors - these are required in order to make the model simulations mirror the incidence graphs and prevalence data from historical outbreaks or epidemics.**

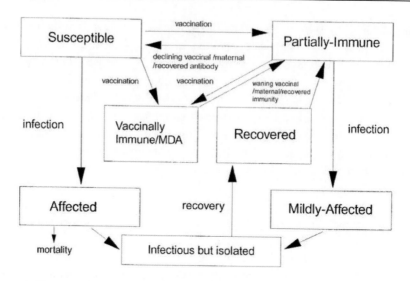

Figure 2. Non-segregated model with optional vaccination programme.

This in turn means that any predictions for future epidemic (or outbreak) prevalence and duration, are generally quantitative guesswork. Second generation biomodels however, [described in Chapter 2] provide factors that are directly measured from the biology (or epidemiology) of the disease. As such, the factors can provide accurate predictions for the disease prevalence and duration of future epidemics (and outbreaks). When the factors are fed into the biomodels, the biomodels can provide accurate epidemiological simulations of future outbreaks or epidemics.

Key concept 2: **The modelling structures of first generation epidemiological models and second generation biomodels are not dissimilar. The significant difference between the first and second generation modelling approaches lies within the use of the directly measured factors that are input into biomodels, but were not available for the first generation models.**

1.4. Matrices

James and Rossiter employed mathematical matrices to model the various disease states that they had identified, such that the collection of these disease states epidemiologically categorised the individuals within a given population, and formed a population (or herd, or flock, etc.) matrix. They also calculated the probabilities whereby an individual in one disease state would transfer to another disease state during a given time period. This in turn generated a probability matrix.

The use of matrices, the inclusion of partially-immune and mildly-affected disease states, and the application of ECRs are discussed in turn, below.

1.5. Probability Matrix and State Vector

The probability matrix is a two dimensional array of rows and columns (Figure 3) and contains the probabilities that an individual in one disease state will transfer to another disease state during a given time period. It is symmetrical (with the same number of rows as columns) since it caters for transitions in either direction between any two disease states.

The state vector is a one dimensional array that records the numbers of individuals within each disease state (Figure 3).

State-transition Technique

state vector   probability matrix   state vector
for time [t]   for time [t+1]

where:

the state vector   = the initial group populations
for time [t]   for time [t],

the probability   = the probabilities of transition
matrix   between groups,

the state vector   = the final group populations
for time [t+1]   for time [t]

Ns = the population of the susceptible group,
Np = the population of the partially-immune group,
Ni = the population of the immune group,
Na = the population of the affected group,
Nm = the population of the mildly-affected group,
and
Nr = the population of the recovered group.

Figure 3. State-transition technique.

1.6. State-Transition Technique

The James-Rossiter model employed a state-transition technique to simulate epidemiological scenarios of disease spread for any given time period. The state vector specified in Figure 3 is overwritten at the end of each time period, after individuals have moved between the various disease states. The number of individuals transferring (or the number of transitions) between respective disease states is calculated by transposing the state vector onto the columns of the probability matrix. Each transposition produces a set of figures for the number of transitions between the specified disease states – the respective transitions are specified by each element of the probability matrix. The transposition process is repeated for all columns in the probability matrix.

1.7. Population Matrix

Monitoring individual individuals through a population matrix facilitates accurate mapping of the natural divisions within a population that might affect the spread of disease. For individuals these divisions include the management segregations within populations or flocks of farmed livestock. For human populations, natural divisions can be geographical, social or even political. A population matrix also records the number of individuals within each disease state.

The population matrix is created as a two dimensional array, with columns to record each individual's identity, and rows to record each individual's epidemiological characteristics. Every individual is assigned a segregation (or division) status, as well as a disease status, by flagging the appropriate row of the population matrix but within its own column.

Subsequently these flags are changed in order to simulate the transitions between disease groups (Figure 2). Group populations at the end of each time interval can then be calculated by summing the respective flags in the population matrix. This approach overcomes difficulties with using fractional probabilities in the probability matrix, since these would in turn yield real values for disease group transitions. Rounding the real num bers to their nearest integer is unacceptable in that it eventually changes the overall size of the population, and population size is a significant epidemiological factor that is correlated with disease prevalence (Anderson and May, 1985).

James and Rossiter (1989) stated that transitions in a stochastic model should inherently be integer because partial individuals cannot be transferred. Moreover, real numbers could not easily be used in conjunction with the population matrix since for individuals it maps gender, age, reproductive status, group age, etc. Dispensing with the population matrix (and thus group age) in favour of real numbers would then require additional disease sub-groups such as 'infected but not infectious', and 'vaccinated but still susceptible': group age tracks these disease sub-groups within the population matrix. The model would therefore be more complex and the reasons for keeping the model simple are discussed later.

Population matrix records for gender and deaths permit the application of birth and mortality rates to the model. Moreover, monitoring an individual's time spent within a group becomes important where group age affects possible transitions elsewhere. For example, vaccinally immune individuals with a declining antibody titre (Figure 2), pass into the partially-immune state when they reach a specific group age. Their population matrix record for group age differentiates them from new entrants to the immune group. Mapping individuals through a population matrix also dispenses with the need to record transition numbers between disease groups, since the disease status of each individual can be examined at the end of every time period. Monitoring subsets of disease groups (age within the group, identification of natural divisions, gender, etc.) is not simple, and a population matrix provides a suitable solution.

1.8. Vaccinal Programme

The second component of disease spread that stems from the Rinderpest model is the accommodation of a vaccinal programme. The inclusion of James-Rossiter's partially-immune state permits the modelling of waning vaccinal immunity, albeit in the form of a transitional status between full protection and susceptibility (Figure 2). Perhaps less significant yet epidemiologically representative is a mildly-affected state (also from the rinderpest model): the mildly-affected state accommodates the outcome of a challenge against partially protected individuals. Partially-immune individuals exhibit reduced clinical signs (under the same challenge) compared to fully susceptible individuals, and thereby justify a separate affected state. The partially-immune group also represents individuals entering the scenario with a level of antibody protection, either through passive immunity or pre-outbreak vaccination.

1.9. R_0 and ECR

The third adaption of the rinderpest model arose from its derivation of an ECR via each time period in the simulation, rather than as a more conventional R_0 across the entire scenario (Anderson and May, 1985): R_0 is defined effectively as the number of disease transmitting contacts between an infected individual and susceptibles in a population. However, ECR is an average of secondary infections from all affected individuals and therefore models the course of the disease past its introduction. Moreover, since ECR is applied to each time interval, it can be subdivided in terms of disease transmission - namely, into contact rate and the effective percentage of those contacts.

First generation modelling includes necessary assumptions. Hence, in applying ECR to each time period it is necessary to assume that ECR remains stable throughout the scenario. For a vaccinated population ECR is also applied to partially-immune individuals [whereas Ro relates only to fully susceptible individuals].

ECRs applied to time intervals do not include the relative population densities of the host, since these are included in Nn:

$$Nn = Nae * ECR * Nh/Nt \qquad \text{(equation i)}$$

where:
Nn = transitions between the non-infected group and the infected group,
Nae = number of individuals excreting virus, and
Nh/Nt = the non-infected group population/population size.

With the above characteristics in mind (sections 1.3 to 1.8), the James-Rossiter approach becomes a useful starting point in the construction of a local or regional epidemiological model. The evolution of a model is also partially dependent upon solutions gleaned from other examples and approaches.

1.10. Model Description

Figure 2 outlines the flow diagram of an initial model based upon six key disease states. The model is essentially a Markov chain, with appropriate compartmentalised disease states and dynamic transitions between them. The transitions are mapped for successive time periods during an epidemic or outbreak simulation (Figure 3). As a state transition model, the starting state vector and probability matrix are initially determined by input parameters (Figure 4) and their recursive values for further time periods are derived from the final state vector and parameters of the preceding period (Searle and Hausman, 1970). The methodology for deriving the state vectors and the probability matrix elements is outlined in Figures 3 and 5.

```
                    Non-Segregated/Optional Vaccination
                    Press F1, Return to abort program
                             Please wait....

Sochastic? Y/N: n
Epidemic period/days: 25
No. susceptibles: 500
No. partially-immune: 200
No. immune: 0
No. affected: 3
No. mildly-affected: 0
No. of vaccination courses: 0
Effective contact rate (recovered): 0.2
Effective contact rate (affected): 3
Effective contact rate (mildly-affected): 1
Immunity (susceptibles): 0.25
Immunity (partially-immune): 0.5
Incubation period (days): 4
Days from infection to end of clinical symptoms: 10


Output data:
```

Day	Susc	P-Imm	Imm	Afft	Maft	NewA	NewM
1	500	200	0	3	0	0	0
2	500	200	0	3	0	0	0
3	500	200	0	3	0	0	0
4	500	200	0	3	0	0	0
5	500	200	0	3	0	5	1
6	495	199	0	8	1	5	1
7	490	198	0	13	2	5	1
8	485	197	0	18	3	5	1
9	480	196	0	23	4	13	3
10	467	193	0	36	7	20	6
11	447	187	0	56	13	26	7
12	421	180	3	79	20	28	8
13	393	172	6	104	28	39	12
14	354	160	9	140	40	54	17
15	300	143	12	191	57	66	22
16	234	121	16	254	78	67	24
17	167	97	20	318	101	62	26
18	105	71	24	377	126	50	25
19	55	46	28	424	150	32	20
20	23	26	43	444	167	15	13
21	8	13	69	439	174	6	7
22	2	6	102	419	174	2	4
23	0	2	138	393	170	0	1
24	0	1	189	354	159	0	1
25	0	0	260	300	143	0	0

Figure 4. Non-segregated/optional vaccination.

To: From:	S	P	I	A	M	R
S	Pss	$V_s*(1-F)$	V_s*F	$1-(1-1/N_s)^{Kni}$ $*(1-V_p)$	0	0
P	$(\tilde{\eta}p(t,vl)/Np)$ $*(1-Ppm)$	Ppp	V_p*F	0	$1-(1-1/Np)^{tni}$ $*(1-V_p)$	0
I	0	$\tilde{\eta}i(t,vl)/Ni$	Pii	0	0	0
A	0	0	0	Paa	0	$\tilde{\eta}a(t,c)/Na$
M	0	0	0	0	Pmm	$\tilde{\eta}m(t,c)/Nm$
R	0	$\tilde{\eta}r(t,w)/Nr$	0	0	0	Prr

where:

```
Pij = the probability of one animal transferring from group i to group j,
a = the affected group,
c = the period from infection to the end of clinical symptoms,
F = the efficacy of the vaccine,
i = the vaccinally immune group,
m = the mildly affected group,
Nx = the current population of x,
ηx(t,g) = the current population of x that have a group age of g at
          time t,
p = the partially-immune group,
r = the recovered group,
s = the susceptible group,
t = the current time period,
vl = the period of waning vaccinal immunity, from an immune to a partially
     -immune titre or from a partially-immune to a susceptible titre,
Vx = the proportion of the group vaccinated at t minus the lag time,
     where lag time denotes the period from vaccinal administration to
     immunity,
w = the period of waning immunity following recovery, to a partially-
    immune titre, and
x = a disease group;
```

$$Nnz = [(ECRa*\Sigma^t_{g=k}\tilde{\eta}a(t,g)) + (ECRm*\Sigma^t_{g=k}\tilde{\eta}m(t,g)) + (ECRr*Nr)] * Nh/Nt$$

with:

```
z = 1, denoting the transitions between the susceptible and affected
    groups,
z = 2, denoting the transitions between the partially-immune and the
    mildly affected groups,
k = the incubation period,
Nh = the current population of group h,
h = s (when z = 1) or p (when z = 2),
Nt = the herd size, and
ECRx is the effective contact rate of x on h.
```

Figure 5. Components of the probability matrix.

1.11. Non-Zero Elements of the Probability Matrix

Psp, Psi and Ppi have a real value whenever vaccination takes effect. Psi and Ppi are derived from both the efficacy of the vaccine and the percentage of group individuals that are vaccinated, whilst Psp comes from the percentage of group individuals vaccinated and one minus the vaccine efficiency. Epidemiologically, an efficient vaccine confers immunity to both susceptible and partially-immune individuals, whereas inefficient immunization moves susceptible individuals into the partially-immune group, leaving partially-immune individuals intransient. The derivations of Psa and Ppm are based upon the James and Rossiter (1989) definitions, with an additional component for vaccination. Pps has a component 1-Ppm, to account for the possibility of infection becoming an influencing factor, since infection will prevent partially-immune individuals (with waning antibody titre) from entering the susceptible group. The important criterion for Pps however, is the number of partially-immune individuals with waning protection levels, either through loss of vaccinal antibodies or in the long term, declining protection after recovery. A similar principle applies to Pip and Prp. Par and Pmr are based upon the period from initial infection to the end of clinical signs. It is also important to note that in calculating Nn_1 and Nn_2 the number of individuals excreting virus is not given by the group populations of Na, Nm and Nr, at the time interval [t - incubation period]; this is due to the possibility of transfers from the groups between the periods [t - incubation] and t. Thus, excretion numbers are computed through current group populations that have a group age $\geq$ the incubation period. Similar reasonings apply to the derivations of Ppa, Ppm, Prp, Pps and Pip.

1.12. Zero Elements of the Probability Matrix

The zero elements without representation (by arrowing) in Figure 2 are:

$$Psm = Psr = 0,$$
$$Ppa = Ppr = 0,$$
$$Pis = Pia = Pim = Pir = 0,$$
$$Pas = Pap = Pai = Pam = 0,$$
$$Pms = Pmp = Pmi = Pma = 0 \text{ and}$$
$$Prs = Pri = Pra = Prm = 0$$

All other elements in the probability matrix are represented in some form in Figure 2, and hence have a real value. The diagonal elements (denoting the probability of an individual retaining its current disease status) are calculated by subtracting the other row elements from one. This is possible because each row corresponds to the probabilities of all transitions from a group, and these must sum to one. Thus:

$$Pss = 1 - Psp - Psi - Psa - Psm - Psr = 1 - Psp - Psi - Psa \qquad \text{(equations ii)}$$

$$Ppp = 1 - Pps - Ppi - Ppa - Ppm = 1 - Pps - Ppi - Ppm \qquad \text{(equations iii)}$$

$$Pii = 1 - Pis - Pip - Pia - Pim - Pir = 1 - Pip \qquad \text{(equations iv)}$$

$$Paa = 1 - Pas - Pap - Pai - Pam - Par = 1 - Par \qquad \text{(equations v)}$$

$$Pmm = 1 - Pms - Pmp - Pmi - Pma - Pmr = 1 - Pmr \qquad \text{(equations vi)}$$

$$Prr = 1 - Prs - Prp - Pri - Pra - Prm = 1 - Prp \qquad \text{(equations vii)}$$

It is important to note that the relevant subtractions cannot be allowed to sum to more than one (since negative probabilities for the diagonals have no meaning), and this is significant in the calculation of Pss where $Psp + Psi + Psa$ must be ≤ 1, and in the computation of Ppp where $Pps + Ppi + Ppm$ must be ≤ 1. In Figures 2 and 5 (and explained more fully below) Pps only models partially-immune individuals not in Ppm, and Ppm only models partially-immune individuals that are not vaccinated. Hence:

$$Pps = \acute{\eta}p \ (t,vl) \ / \ Np \ (1 - Ppm)$$

This could also be written:

$$\acute{\eta}p \ / \ Np \ (1 - Ppm) \qquad \text{(equation viii)}$$

where $\acute{\eta}p$ is the number of partially-immune individuals currently showing waning vaccinal immunity (Figure 5). $\acute{\eta}p$ is dependent upon Np, the current partially-immune group population and $\acute{\eta}p \ / \ Np$ will always be ≤ 1. This being the case, (outside the days that vaccination takes effect, where $Ppi = 0$) as $\acute{\eta}p \ / \ Np \rightarrow 1$, then $Pps \rightarrow (1 - Ppm)$. Inserting $Pps \rightarrow (1 - Ppm)$ into equation (iii) above:

$$Ppp \rightarrow 1 - Pps - 0 - Ppm = 1 - (1 - Ppm) - Ppm = 0 \qquad \text{(equation ix)}$$

and Ppp will not be negative.

Alternatively, if ńp / Np < 1 (which is more likely), then Ppp may have a real value. Mathematically, equation (ix) defines the limits of Ppp. Epidemiologically the disease will attack partially-immune individuals regardless of their vaccinal protection and induce a mild form of the disease. Thus, the probability of partially-immune individuals with (waning immunity) contracting the disease will be ńp / Np (Ppm), and for those that become susceptible will be ńp / Np (1 - Ppm). The remaining element in the row Ppp plays only a 'passive' role in these calculations (1 – Ppi – Ppm - Pps), since partially-immune individuals do not remain in their group if challenged or when losing immunity.

On the days that vaccination takes effect the value for Ppi will not be zero and must therefore be included in the calculation of Ppp. However, Ppm is dependent upon Ppi (by virtue of Ppm having the component 1-Ppi) since vaccination prevents transition from partial-immunity to mildly-affected status (Figure 2.5); Pps is in turn, dependent upon Ppm, because Pps has the component 1-Ppm (reflecting the precedence of infection preventing any individuals re-entering the susceptible group). Hence, Ppi+Ppm+Pps cannot exceed one, so Ppp will not be negative. A similar reasoning applies to the calculation of Pss, where Psp and Psa are dependent upon Psi, and Pss cannot become negative. All rows in the probability matrix therefore fulfil the requirement of summing to one.

1.13. Notation

The notation can be rearranged to resemble alternative formats used in the literature.

Hence,

$Nj' = \sum Ni.Pij$ can be re-written as

$$Nj' = \sum Pji.Ni$$

where Nj' is an element of the final state vector for time period t, Ni is an element of the starting state vector at t, and Pji is the transposal of the probability matrix Pij.

1.14. Stochasticism and Transitions

Monte-Carlo stochasticism (Shreider, 1966) is applied to the transitions, from the susceptible/ partially-immune groups to the affected/ mildly-affected states respectively. For each group the expected population at time t + 1 is:

$$Nj' = \sum Ni.Pij \qquad \text{(equation x)}$$

and the expected number of individuals transferring between two of the groups becomes:

$$E = Ni.Pij \qquad \text{(equation xi)}$$

Thus, combining (x) and (xi) gives:

$$Nj' = \sum E$$

However, E will often be a real number and where a population matrix is constructed to represent individuals this cannot easily be reflected in moving partial individuals. Since the importance of retaining the population matrix has been previously outlined [re monitoring disease group subsets] E could be rounded to the nearest integer value. Nevertheless, the difficulty with integerisation is that it cannot always be justified epidemiologically. In the absence of stochasticism, a deterministic or average outcome is being modelled and integerisation in this instance may introduce a compound error during the course of a scenario. Although the error will be less significant as E increases, an effective solution arises in the introduction of vectors (described later) to replace the population matrix, when real numbers would be expected. Determinism is used within the model where $E \geq 10$, since a stochastic element for large values of E would impose high processing demands during runtime. Epidemiologically, chance is less important if the group transfer is large, so where $E \geq 10$ simple integerisation will suffice and the application of stochasticism is unnecessary. On the other hand, if <10 individuals are expected to move, then the effects of chance become more significant, and to add a stochastic element to the computations, a random number ($0 \leq R \leq 1$) is compared to the cumulative probability of E = 0, E = 1, E = 2..E = Ni, until:

$$\sum_{Ei=0}^{Ni} P[Ei] > R \qquad \text{(equation xii)}$$

where E' is taken as the highest value of Ei, and the range of values for E' will follow a Binomial distribution (Ahlbom, 1993), with a modal value of E (equation xi).

P[Ei] can be calculated from the Binomial formula (Burghes and Wood, 1980):

$$P[Ei] = (Ni! \, / \, Ei! \, \{Ni - Ei\}!) \, P^{Ei} \, (1 - P)^{Ni-Ei} \qquad \text{(equation xiii)}$$

where P is the probability of a transition Pij.

The estimated values of E' then have to be implemented across the population matrix to effect the transfers, and a random selection from within the respective disease groups would ensure that the selections are realistic: realistic in the sense that no bias would be developed for vaccinal history, group age, etc., as might be the case if the selections were made by ascending or descending individual number. Thus, selections for transitions should be made randomly.

When Pij is small but Ni is large, the value of Ni! in equation (xiii) becomes unmanageable (by exceeding the integer limit for programming), and the Poisson approximation is used instead (Thrusfield, 1995).

Hence, $P[Ei] = N.P^{Ei}.e^{-NP} / \, Ei!$

The importance of Binomial and Poisson formulae in the stochastic function, is that they reduce the overall number of usual Monte-Carlo comparisons required (Eij = $\sum^{Ni}_{k=0}$ Pij $\geq$ R_k), whilst not nullifying the stochasticism itself. This is because although they dispense with the need to make additional comparisons once condition (xii) has been satisfied, they are not employed to determine the modal or most common value for E' (which would nullify the stochastic effect).

1.15. Group Segregations or Divisions

As previously discussed there is a need for segregated groups (or natural divisions) within models to be modelled as discrete entities, with differential ECRs, probability matrices and state vectors. Figure 6 describes possible criteria that could be used to measure disease transmission between segregated divisions. Every segregated group effectively becomes a spatial sub-model, and its parameters are recalculated for each time period. The incidence between the groups could be mapped by array, and would represent a significant 'bottleneck' to disease transmission within the population. The input data for segregated groups may be entered sequentially according to the probable route of transmission, with the assumption that there is negligible 'back transmission' of the disease. This is justified, by the fact that disease passage through a division will outpace the spread between them, hence 'donor' divisions will have become fully infected before 'backward transfer' from the 'recipient' group(s) becomes significant. An alternative approach to modelling the segregated groups discretely is to use a single model with the same probability matrix and state vectors. For each time interval, the incidence is determined through the disease group transitions of the non-segregated model, and then apportioned to segregated group individuals that fall within the appropriate disease groups. For example, if the number of transitions from susceptibility to affected status (at time t) was computed to be ten, ten individuals flagged as susceptibles in the population matrix would be re-flagged as affected: the selection of which ten would be dependent upon their record denoting segregation number, and the weighting applied to that segregation. Weightings should reflect the proximity of the group to the source of infection (by the ratio of its spatial perimeter adjoining the infected group with its own overall segregation perimeter), and also its pen stocking density. The disadvantage of this approach is that the level of incidence is determined by the non-segregated model, excluding the effects of 'bottlenecking' between segregations. Moreover, indirect estimations of bottlenecks would reintroduce an immeasurable parameter into the modelling. Thus for local epidemiological models discrete entities or sub-models are the preferred option.

1.16. Simplification

Two disease groups modelling 'removed affected' individuals, and 'removed mildly-affected' individuals have been incorporated into the flow diagram (Figure 7). However, there is no requirement to actually model them. This is because the individuals become 'isolated yet still infectious' (Figure 2) before entering the absorbing status of recovery. The 'isolated yet infectious' state can be omitted altogether by reducing the infectious period, from onset of pathogen excretion to the end of clinical signs (Figure 8). Hence, isolated individuals that are no longer spreading disease are categorised within the recovered group. The justification for this assumption, is because isolated individuals do not affect the epidemiology of the disease, and so long as the correct number of individuals pass from infected to recovered status, the population size is also properly maintained. It is possible to model both the vaccinally immune and recovered individuals within a single 'immune' group, using an array in the population matrix to denote recovered status. However, whilst this is a programming possibility, such an oversimplification would fail to denote the important distinctions between vaccinally immune and recovered individuals - for example the differential levels of antibody protection and duration of immunity, and the long-term carriage of disease.

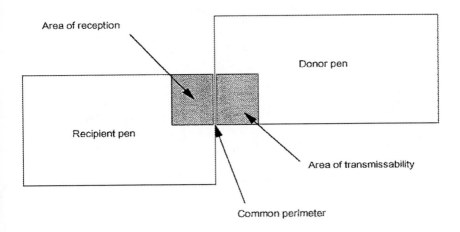

Na or the number of affecteds in area of transmissability = [(cp * dt) / dpa] * NA
and
Ns or the number of challenged susceptibles in the area of reception = [(cp * dr) / rpa] * NS
where
cp = common perimeter,
dpa = donor pen area,
dr = depth of receptive area,
dt = depth of transmissability area,
NA = number of affected animals in donor pen,
NS = number of susceptibles in recipient pen, and
rpa = recipient pen area.

Figure 6. Estimating the transition rate of disease between segregated farm pens.

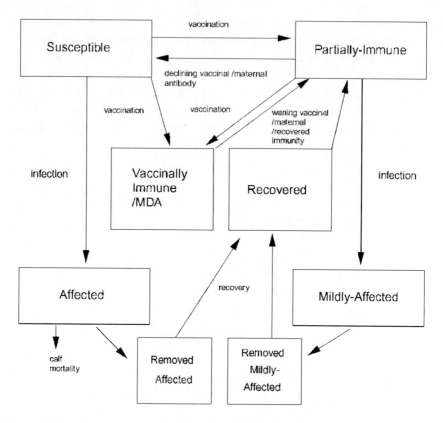

Figure 7. Flow diagram of model showing redundant disease groups.

1.17. Model Parameters

The model output from simulation scenarios should ideally match the format of the quantitative data from the field. This will facilitate comparisons between the simulations and the field data in a subsequent validation of the model. For local disease models the available field data is primarily supplied by the farming community, research projects and national health services. Natural segregations are regularly imposed upon the susceptible populations, and include categories such as age group or reproductive status. The model output should therefore reflect these divisions in monitoring disease incidence, and the incidence may likewise be tabulated to reflect the divisions. One of the difficulties in processing input data within a model is that any oversimplifications can lead towards a bias of results. For example, amalgamating the input from a vaccinated segregated population into a non-segregated format, may fail to account for spatial heterogeneity. This could subsequently inflate the overall levels of incidence through the absence of spatial disease 'bottlenecks', since bottlenecking is an inherent imposition of natural or managed segregations. It also provides time for post-outbreak vaccinations to reach and protect the uninfected portions of the population. Anderson and May (1985) have pointed out that ECRs vary according to segregational group, and are inaccurately represented by an overall ECR for the non-segregated model. A general ECR would therefore affect the accuracy of simulating group incidence. The disparity caused by using a non segregated model on segregated data is indicative of the need to model natural or management segregations. A heterogeneous population could also be modelled as a single segregation group. If two identical simulations using the segregated and non-segregated models were to show insignificant disparity, perhaps the segregational component of the model could be excluded. Irrespective of any similarity in incidence levels (for the two models), segregational components do however map the spread of the disease through the population, and therefore make an important contribution to the examination of local spread.

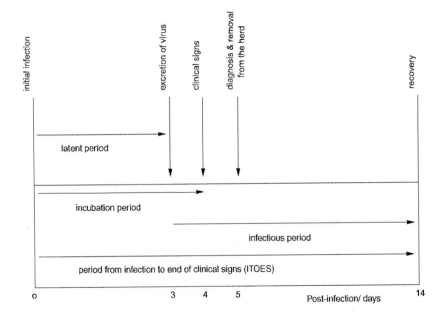

Figure 8. Chronology of FMD (adapted from Tinline, 1972).

1.18. Disease Group Populations at Time t_0

The majority of a population (at time t_0) enters the partially-immune or susceptible disease groups. However, the proportions of this division are potentially prone to error and the difficulty lies in both defining each group, and accounting for the variability of pre-outbreak vaccination programmes. Partially-immune individuals could be defined as those with an antibody titres falling within a predetermined range. This range would confer partial protection to the group and only yield a mild form of the disease. The definition is somewhat complicated by the challenge level or pathogen output from source, with a high challenge required to infect partially-immune individuals and a low challenge sufficient to infect fully susceptible individuals (Figure 9). For the purposes of the state-transition model (and apart from transmission via carrier individuals) a high challenge level is assumed. The antibody titre range for susceptibles would apply to individuals showing severe clinical signs. An alternative definition of partial-immunity could be any individuals that had been vaccinated or carried an antibody titre. Susceptibles would then become individuals with a zero level of antibody titre (Figure 10). One of the consequences of not using range definition becomes apparent during model runtime. If a vaccinal programme was to be introduced into a scenario, all susceptible individuals would become partially-immune by virtue of gaining an antibody titre. This in turn would drop the number of resultant affected individuals to zero (to be replaced by mildly-affected cases), and the true incidence of severe disease would be masked. This may or may not be epidemiologically accurate. Alternatively, with a range definition susceptible individuals are permitted a shallow range of protection titre, and following vaccination affected cases may still appear. It is interesting to note that whilst for most scenarios the distinction between affected and mildly-affected cases may not be significant, the option to detail this difference could prove to be important.

Returning to the problem of disease group distributions within a population, the difficulty is compounded further by a possibility of an ineffective vaccine having been used in prophylactic programmes. The programme itself may also have been poorly administered. Low efficacy vaccines or vaccines that were incorrectly administered to control the wrong strain of virus, would bias disease group distributions. Where neither was catered for in the model, there would be a positive bias in the proportion of individuals entering the partially-immune group, and this would inaccurately inflate population immunity. Poorly administered vaccinal programmes would have a similar yet less severe effect. Efficient prophylactic vaccination of (parts of) the population also affects the disease groups into which individuals are placed. Vaccinal programmes administered longer ago than the critical inter-vaccination period (CIP) will yield individuals in the population with diminishing antibody protection - the level of vaccinal protection will continue to drop below immunity unless a booster vaccination programme is administered. Individuals vaccinated beyond that time would most probably be immune or partially-immune, although there is difficulty in assessing an appropriate protection level.

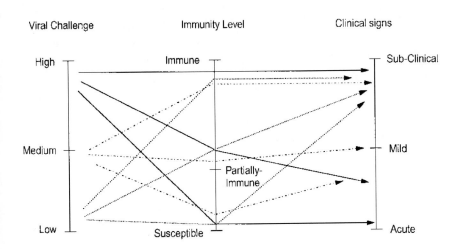

Figure 9. The impact of viral challenge and host immunity upon disease expression.

Gibbs (1994, unpublished) outlined the relative numbers of immune, partially-immune and susceptible individuals found within segregated age groups. Although his results specifically included programmes of previous vaccination, this did not preclude the possibility of further work calculating the distribution populations for other vaccination programmes. Such data would facilitate apportioning of the population into disease groups at time t_0. Additional model input parameters are required in the use of the Gibbs data. These include segregated group populations and the number of initial cases within each group. All individuals from an unvaccinated population would enter the simulation as susceptibles, and vaccination of recovered individuals would boost their immunity. A retrospective mode of apportioning population individuals to disease groups is by observing the final percentage of individuals that are infected and hence exhibiting clinical signs (Figure 11, bottom rows). The higher the percentage of incidence in an age group (or segregation: see Figure 11 top row), the more of the group's individuals are marked as susceptible. The lower the incidence, the more are apportioned to a partially-immune status. The reasoning behind this rationale is that a group (or segregation) with low disease incidence, is likely to possess greater average immunity than a group with high incidence. The division of any segregation into susceptible and partially-immune disease groups would be arbitrary. It would be consistent though, given a predetermined formula relating incidence to the division ratio. Serological data by Gibbs (unpublished) provided a mode of estimating disease group distributions within the segregations. The only limiting factor in the Gibbs data was that it related specifically to immunity levels produced by one vaccination programme. A method of quantifying immunity levels is thus required, irrespective of the vaccinal programme employed.

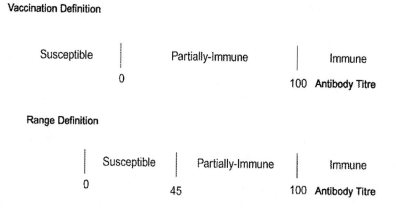

Figure 10. Defining susceptibles and partially-immune individuals within the model.

Age/Lt	0-3	4-6	7-16	17-24	1	2	3	4	5	6	7	8	9	Bull	Tot.
Pop.	39	74	255	272	342	312	207	147	89	58	30	10	2	8	1845
*26.9						1									1
*27.9															
28.9					1	2									3
29.9					1	2	2	1							6
30.9					4	4									8
1.10					3	5	4	1	1						14
2.10						1									1
3.10				11		3	1								15
4.10				31	22	8	3	2				1			67
5.10				50	37	5	5	2					:		100
*6.10					39	15	6	3	3			1			67
7.10					34	41	11	12	9	5	3	1		2	118
8.10			12		37	22	9	16	6	3	4	1			110
*9.10					15	11	10	12			1	1			50
10.10			3		1	9	3	3		1	1				32
11.10		4			6	9	2	4	1		1				27
12.10	1	8			1		2	1			1				14
13.10		4	8												12
14.10		5	3												8
15.10		5	6			1									12
16.10		3	3												6
17.10			3												3
18.10		3	2												5
19.10		3													3
20.10	2	1	1										:		4
21.10		3	2												5
22.10		5													5
23.10		3													3
24.10		4	1												5
25.10		1													1
26.10		1	1												2
27.10		1													1
29.10	2														2
%inftd	8	58	21	77	54	26	34	23	61	17	17	20	50	38	38%
Tot.	3	43	54	209	185	80	71	33	10	10	5	2	1	3	709

* A significant drop in incidence due to vaccination, is expected
on 30.9.92 following vaccination on 26.9.92 and 27.9.92.
However, the effect is apparent on 6.10.92 or possibly 9.10.92.

Figure 11. Example of the extended vaccinal lag time in Saudi Arabian FMD epidemics (Al Kharj, 1992).

A noteworthy observation at this point arises in the role of individuals incubating the disease, since these individuals would be subclinically infected at time t_0. Incubating individuals could be placed in the affected or mildly-affected disease groups, rather than into the partially-immune or susceptible groups. A problem however arises in estimating their group age, as this should reflect the length of incubation period that has already expired by t_0. It may also be difficult to determine the number of individuals incubating the disease at time t_0.

1.19. Immunity Levels

Pre-outbreak levels of antibodies and vaccinal titres gained during an outbreak, play an important role in the epidemiology of disease modelling. One method of modelling immunity is by applying an immunity weighting to Nn, where:

Nn is the number of transitions from the partially-immune/susceptible states to the mildly-affected/affected groups.

Since individual and group antibody titres are measurable directly, an accurate immunity weighting could be introduced into the model. The susceptible group are assumed to be those individuals falling within a predetermined antibody titre range, and therefore have an immunity weighting (rather than none at all). The strength of the immunity for both the partially-immune and susceptibles is reflected reciprocally in the weighting, and this produces a fraction of the original value for Nn:

swt = 1 − immunity [s], piwt = 1 − immunity [pi]   (equations xiv)
Nn1 = Nn1 * swt, Nn2 = Nn2 * piwt   (equations xv)

where swt is the immunity weighting for the susceptible group, and piwt is the weighting for partially-immune individuals. The model is more sensitive to changes in the weighting than in ECR, and immunity thereby becomes a versatile tool in affecting the epidemiology of the simulation. This is due to the fact that any changes in weighting are applied simultaneously to all three ECRs (for recovered, mildly-affected and affected individuals), whereas the ECR's themselves are altered independently:

Nn1 = ((ECR[r]*e[r])+(ECR[m]*e[m])
+(ECR[a]*e[a]))*swt*Ns/Nt   (equation xvi)

where e[x] = number of recovered, mildly-affected or affected individuals excreting the pathogen, and Ns/Nt = number of susceptibles / population size. Thus, changing ECR[r] will have no impact upon ECR[m] or ECR[a], and little impact on Nn1. However, changing swt will affect ECR[r], ECR[m] and ECR[a], and therefore significantly alter Nn1. For simulation purposes, pre-outbreak dates of vaccinal programmes are indicative of the initial immunity within a population. Gibbs (unpublished) measured the range and mean antibody titres for segregated age groups. Despite the fact that the population had previously been vaccinated according to a specific programme, similar data covering alternative vaccination regimes could facilitate estimations of immunity for any population. Direct measurement of antibody titres would also avoid immunity weightings becoming immeasurable parameters (IMP). Unvaccinated populations are given zero values for immunity.

1.20. Waning Immunity

Waning vaccinal immunity becomes an important model feature whenever the length of the simulation is significant compared to the half-life for the protecting antibody (Kitching and Salt, 1995). In such circumstances, failure to account for waning antibody would underestimate the level of disease incidence. If the simulation is short with respect to the half-life, then there will be little effect of falling protection on incidence. The same assumptions apply to waning maternally-derived antibodies (MDA) in young individuals, although the young can have a vulnerable stage during MDA loss, where MDA protection is low but passive immunity inhibits the production of antibodies to vaccines (Kitching and Salt, 1995). Waning immunity is modelled by appropriately reducing the immunity weighting (between time intervals) according to antibody half-life, and the rates for diminishing protection in recovered, vaccinally-immune and partially-immune individuals are fixed independently, since they cannot be assumed to be equal.

1.21. Measurable Parameters for ECR

An alternative to the use of immunity weightings for Nn is to include the effect of antibody titres upon the level of ECR. The resultant impact on the simulation is the same, since swt can become a component of ECR, and ECR can be re-written with measurable parameters, eliminating it as an IMP.

ECR = CR * %effective contacts between hosts and an infected

= CR * swt   (equation xvii)

where CR is the contact rate between hosts and an infected.

Key concept 3: The value for ECR is effectively derived from the contact rate [between hosts and an infected individual] and the level of host immunity [which can be measured directly via vaccine efficacy or antibody titre]. However, whilst measuring components of ECR improves accuracy, it does not overcome the compound errors accumulated by estimating quantitative values for multiple factors (or components) within a model. The optimal solution is to measure a factor that is accurately correlated with the required output, such as prevalence or incidence.

ECR by definition is the number of effective contacts between full susceptibles and an infected animal, hence the value of swt in equation (xvii) above must be 100% successful or 1, for unvaccinated populations. Nevertheless, to apply ECR to the vaccinated population, equations (xvi) and (xvii) can be combined. Thus, substituting ECR = CR * swt into equation (xvi):

$$\{(CR[r]*e[r]*swt)+(CR[m]*e[m]*swt)+ \\ (CR[a]*e[a]*swt)\}*Ns/Nt = Nn1 \qquad \text{(equation xviii)}$$

Contact rate and the immunity weighting in equation (xviii) above are still both fully measurable parameters.

By splitting swt into components for recovered, mildly-affected and affected individuals, differential values for swt[r], swt[m] and swt[a] can be ascribed:

$$\{(CR[r]*e[r]*swt[r])+(CR[m]*e[m]*swt[m])+(CR[a]*e[a]*swt[a]\} \\ *Ns/Nt = Nn1 \qquad \text{(equation xix)}$$

Swt[r], swt[m] and swt[a] are seemingly identical since immunity is dependent upon the antibody titre of the hosts rather than the viral output of recovered, mildly-affected or affected individuals. However, the importance of differential values for swt[r], swt[m] and swt[a] becomes apparent when considering the interaction of immunity and pathogen challenge on swt. The use of swt[] has so far been described in the calculation of Nn1, or the effect of challenge on susceptible individuals. However, the same principles can be applied to Nn2, the effect of challenge on partially-immune individuals, and a similar set of equations to (xvi) to (xviii) would be produced using Nn2.

1.22. Pathogen Challenge

Nn1 is not solely dependent upon the host immunity to infection; the level of virus excreted from diseased individuals also plays a significant role. Figure 9 outlines the interactions of immunity and pathogen challenge (in this instance viral) that are likely to produce disease transmission (between infected and host individuals). Figure 12 suggests a possible mode of calculating swt[] and pwt[] from a given level of viral challenge, with the mean and range of antibody titre for the host group in question. The definition of swt has thus been extended to include the effect of challenge from infected individuals (as well as retaining the impact of immunity from the host population). Hence, permitting differential values of swt[r], swt[m] and swt[a] caters for the variety of virus excretion levels exhibited by recovered, mildly-affected and affected individuals, and may enhance the accuracy of the model. Whereas swt[] refers to the susceptible group weighting, pwt [] is applied to the partially-immune group; pwt is substituted for swt in equation (xvii), and equation (xvii) is used to calculate Nn2 in (xvi) in the same way as Nn1. The significance of immunity in Figure 12 is that it indicates the proportion of individuals succumbing to a given level of challenge. The effects of swt [r] and pwt[r] will be small, since recovered individuals usually excrete insufficient virus to infect host individuals.

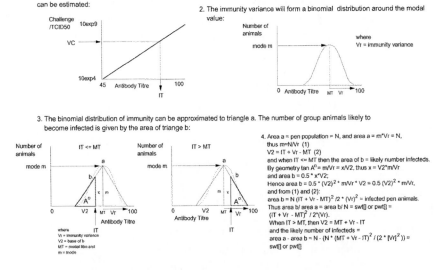

Figure 12. Calculating swt[] and pwt[].

1.23. Pathogen Excretion

The number of individuals excreting pathogen is computed by those affected and mildly-affected individuals with a group age sufficient for pathogen production (Figure 8). The incubation period is usually pathogen-free for viral diseases, so that the onset of clinical signs normally accompanies virus production and contagiousness. However, some infectious diseases spread rapidly and this rapidity is in part, enhanced by individuals becoming infectious before the advent of clinical signs (during the incubation period). The consequence of this early production of pathogen is that infected individuals cannot be easily isolated before they become contagious. Therefore, since diseased individuals can produce secondary infections within the final days of the incubation period (Figure 8), this can be modelled via a suitable (mildly-affected/affected) group age for pathogen production.

1.24. Contact Rate

The direct measurability of contact rate is an essential constituent in determining ECRs for recovered, mildly-affected and affected individuals. CR (equation xvii) is the number of contacts between one infected animal and (any) uninfected individuals within the same segregated area. A theoretical possibility for CR is outlined below:

CR $\approx$ stock density * population % of uninfected individuals

Hence, with a linear relationship between stock density and CR:

$$CR = k_{cr} * N/Asp * Ns/N = k_{cr} * Ns/Asp \text{ or}$$
$$CR = f(N/Asp) Ns/N \text{ (non-linear)} \hspace{2cm} \text{(equation xx)}$$

where:

k_{cr} = a constant calculated by plotting CR against pen stocking density, for one individual amongst uninfected individuals:

$$k_{cr} = CR/(N/Asp) \text{ when } Ns/N = 1 \text{ or } Ns = N$$

These values could be determined by observation.
N = the number of individuals within a segregated pen,
Ns = the number of susceptibles within a segregated pen, and

Asp = the area of the segregated pen.

It is interesting to note that N/Asp (stock density) has a differential effect from Ns/N (the proportion of susceptible individuals within a pen) - see equation (xvi). Whilst the former is dependent upon pen size and introduces a spatial element, the latter is determined by the size of the disease group.

Key concept 4: **Spatial factors were introduced latterly into first generation disease modelling and have become useful in improving epidemiological realism.**

CR may increase linearly with stocking density (SD), reach a peak and then fall as weight of numbers spatially inhibits the free movement of uninfected individuals. It may be unlikely that farm pens would be stocked beyond the CR peak level. The value for the constant k_{cr} could be determined experimentally or measured from field data, however there is to date, no experimental data to calculate the value of the function f(N/Asp). There are though a number of indicators to CR in the literature.

Hafez et al. (1969) have categorised the different forms of behaviour exhibited by cattle, and some of these will initiate interaction or contact between population individuals - grooming, licking and agonistic behaviour (O'Connell et al., 1989). Behavioural patterns have been observed by Fraser (1980) that could allow average daily interactions to be calculated per animal, and Wierenga (1984) has reported that increasing pen stocking density elevates agonistic behaviour whilst having no effect on social licking. Moreover, cattle at pasture interact differently from those in confined enclosures (Wierenga and Metz, 1986). For example individuals in confined conditions will synchronise their behavioural patterns to a lesser degree than when grazing (Metz and Wierenga, 1986). Pen shape and stocking density also affects the way that cattle position themselves within a pen (Stricklin et al., 1979) since cattle tend to keep their heads to the perimeter, only using the centre when traffic is heavier (Curtis and Houpt, 1983).

All these factors affect the level and frequency of social interaction between population individuals. Wierenga (1984) measures social licking at approximately 3 interactions per animal per 24 hours. Agonistic behaviour ranges from 2 interactions per animal per day at pasture, to 7-10 interactions in enclosures (dependent upon the stocking density). Adding interactions for licking behaviour to those for agonistic encounters, places CR at 5 interactions per animal per day at pasture, and 10-13 interactions for enclosed individuals. The latter figure of 10-13 interactions may be high for CR in the sense that it includes a high proportion of agonistic encounters, and agonistic behaviour is a less likely to allow disease transmission than the close physical proximity of social licking. Nevertheless the literature suggests that CR may be between 5-13 daily interactions per animal, irrespective of population environment.

1.25. Segregation

The differentiation between a segregated and non-segregated simulation is achieved by specifying the number of population divisions to be higher than or equal to one.

1.26. Areas of Reception and Transmissibility

Transmission between segregations (CR_2) [and in this instance farm pens] is effected in a similar way to intra-segregational transmission, commencing with the identification of a donor and a recipient pen.

Hence, taking the transmission area to be a third pen:

$$CR_2 = k_{cr} * Ns/Asp_1 * A_1/Asp_1 * A_2/Asp_2 = k_{cr}$$
$$* Ns/Asp_2 \ (A^2/Asp_1^2) \hspace{2cm} \text{(equation xxi)}$$

where:

$A = A_1 = A_2$ since the transmission area should be divided equally between A_1 and A_2,

k_{cr} = the same constant described above for intra-pen transmission,

Ns/Asp, = the stock density of uninfecteds (similar to intra-pen transmission),

A_1/Asp_1 = the likelihood of Ns to be in the area of reception,

A_2/Asp_2 = the likelihood of a challenge animal to be in the area of transmissibility,

Ns = the number of susceptibles within the recipient segregation,

Asp_1 = the recipient pen area,

Asp_2 = the donor pen area,

A_1 = the area of reception and

A_2 = the area of transmissibility.

Since backward transmission between pens is considered negligible, all recipient pens will contain uninfected individuals and therefore Ns/N = 100% or 1 (equation xx): Ns/N is thus redundant. However, backward transmission can be incorporated into the model. The partial mobility of an infected animal does not alter its likelihood of being within the area of transmissibility, since a slower individual is likely to spend as much time within the transmission region as a fully mobile one. Hence mobility will not affect CR between pens.

1.27. Serotype

There is a possibility that the vaccinal input parameters (for vaccine efficiency, and other factors) used in the model may be inappropriate. This could occur where the vaccine administered is an incorrect serotype for the outbreak (Brooksby, 1986; Bachrach, 1977). However, such a scenario is unlikely in that disease incidence tends to be of a single serotype, and easily identifiable (Kitching, 1995; Kitching et al., 1988; Samuel et al., 1990). A problem may arise in the emergence of a heterologous strain (Brooksby, 1968) and this could result in poor matching of the vaccine to the pathogen strain.

1.28. Time Interval

The choice of time interval used for the simulation scenarios has relevance to the degree of detail that is required in the epidemiology. A short interval reveals more detail, whilst a large interval is less processor intensive for simulation runtime. The most convenient period length is probably a day for outbreaks and a fortnight (or a week) for epidemics. The length of time interval is ultimately suggested by the format of the available field data, since for ease of comparison field data and simulation parameters should match as closely as possible.

1.29. Incubation Period and Vaccination

Donaldson (1987) has pointed out that the incubation period can decrease during the course of an epidemic as the level of pathogen excretion increases, and this is modelled through appropriate input parameters (Figure 4). The expected lag time between an administration of vaccine and the onset of vaccinal immunity, typically has a range of a few days but can extend to longer periods of time. At the end of the lag period sufficient antibodies have usually been produced to confer a level of protection (namely, full immunity or partial immunity to a subsequent disease challenge). The lag time can become inflated and the scale of this increase is dependent upon how many other individuals are incubating the disease, and also for how long at the time of initial diagnosis and subsequent vaccinal administration. If the disease has already become established in the population, the effect of the vaccine (on incidence) will only become apparent when all the 'incubators' (outside vaccinal protection) have been diagnosed and isolated. Incidence will then fall as the disease contacts vaccinally protected individuals that were disease-free at the time of vaccination.

A likely reason for consistently high lag times lies in the mode of disease introduction. A disease challenge may infect just one or two individuals in a population, and so long as their diagnosis and isolation are prompt, most of the population will respond to effective vaccination. Typically, this form of disease source may be derived from foodstuffs or through the introduction of individuals incubating the disease, to a susceptible pool. However, where the disease source infects a large number of the population together, or consistently infects population members within a short period of time, the diagnosis of incidence will only be made after the disease is established. Correspondingly, vaccinal programmes that are implemented after this 'late' diagnosis, will protect just a portion of the population, and an increased vaccination lag time will be apparent until all the 'incubators' have shown clinical disease.

Some populations are particularly vulnerable to this latter mode of infection, wherever the susceptible pool comes into close contact with travelling individuals or nomadic livestock, since these individuals offer a constant source of possible infection. One solution to the problem of increased vaccinal lag, lies in improved disease security. Monitoring transport vehicles and screening individuals for disease (especially when they make new contacts with a susceptible pool), decreases the likelihood of an outbreak or epidemic. Protecting susceptible pools from possible disease carriers can effectively be achieved through geographical or spatial barriers. Reducing vaccinal lag time will likewise afford a susceptible population additional protection. Moreover, restricting disease spread at its source permits post-outbreak vaccination programmes to be implemented before an epidemic can become established, and this in turn can enhance the cessation of incidence should an epidemic occur.

1.30. Carriers

A model can be run over an extended period of time to determine the effects of carriers on disease persistence. The causality of carriers is currently unclear for some diseases, and possibly difficult to model (Graves et al., 1971; Trautman and Sutmoller, 1971). Moreover, the significant factors in the re-emergence of disease through carriers, need to be identified before they can be measured. The carrier state in both vaccinated and unvaccinated individuals can continue for many months or longer (Kitching, 1992; Radostits et al., 1994). Carriers can be modelled by assigning a low viral output to recovered individuals, and at an insufficient level to induce clinical signs in susceptible from a single recovered individual. It is possible that where multiple carriers concurrently provide a disease challenge against a susceptible, that susceptible individuals may succumb to the cumulative challenge of the carriers as they excrete the pathogen. However to date, it has not been possible to prove this experimentally.

1.31. Model Complexity

A difficulty that arises in the use of a state-transition technique is the complexity of the model. Spatial segregations that are an integral part of modelling topography have been shown to play a significant role in the regulation of disease transmission. Thus they cannot logically be excluded from local or regional disease modelling. However, model complexity is increased substantially by the introduction of population segregations and a state-transition model for FMD may prove more useful as a general tool in estimating the final level of population %infected, rather than mapping the details of transmission across population segregations. Moreover, this adaption would require fewer input parameters and necessitate a shorter runtime. A more complex model can be developed using vectors rather than disease state transitions.

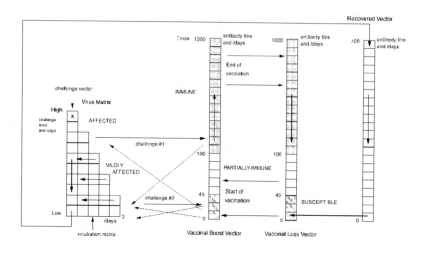

Figure 13. Vector transition modelling.

1.32. Modelling with Vectors

A solution to the problem of model complexity (imposed by population segregations) appears with the modification of the state-transition approach into vector-transition (Figure 13). Vector-transition retains the disease states and their interactions, however the disease is modelled in a more continuous rather than discrete form. This is because disease states can be merged within the disease vectors. The immune group for example, in Figure 13 covers a section of the vaccinal loss vector and a section of the vaccinal boost vector. The same applies to partially-immune and susceptible groupings, and the virus matrix is partitioned into affected and mildly-affected sections. The recovered vector is not partitioned. The interactions between states (Figure 7) need no longer be determined by a probability matrix. Some of the transitions between disease states occur through daily ascent/descent of the vectors (Figure 13), while all of the others are determined by inter-vector transitions. One of the disadvantages in employing a population matrix to map individuals is the heightened processing load that is required with a larger population size (20,000 or more individuals). This is reflected in an increased computer run-time for the working model. The use of distribution vectors constitutes an alternative to the population matrix, in that it models the labyrinth of immunity levels exhibited by the partially-immune group. Vector (or array) elements represent levels of protection found in the group, as population individuals ascend or descend their lengths. This in turn provides greater flexibility and accuracy in modelling both antibody titres and the interaction between disease challenge and immunity. Similarly the range of pathogen production from affected and mildly-affected individuals can be modelled by vector, shifting the representation of infection from clinical signs to pathogen output. This also improves flexibility in defining the severity of the clinical signs and the extent of pathogen production. Affected and mildly-affected individuals can thus fall within a range of elements specified on the virus matrix (Figure 13) - the virus matrix can similarly accommodate other pathogens.

1.33. Vector-Transition Technique

In Figure 13 the vaccinal vectors are subdivided into a pre-defined number of titre segments with individuals passing *en bloc* to the adjacent segment each day (as their protection wanes according to antibody half-life, or rises steadily after vaccination). The vaccinal boost vector individuals (starting from day 1 post-vaccination) ascend one or more segments per day, whilst the vaccinal loss vector individuals (commencing from day 1 of antibody decline post-vaccination) descend one or more segments every day. Post-vaccination antibody rapidly rises to a peak, and then slowly declines. Unvaccinated individuals remain at the foot of the vaccinal loss vector. The disease status of an individual is dependent upon both the vector within which it is found in and its position within that vector. All population individuals fall within one of the four vectors outlined in Figure 13.

The division of the vaccinal vectors into disease groups is pre-determined by threshold titre values. For example, $100/r_1$ (and above) for immune individuals, $45/r_1$ - $100/r_1$ for partially-immune, and any individuals below $45/r_1$ are assumed to be fully susceptible, where:

r_1 = antibody titre against heterologous virus/
antibody titre against homologous virus

Since segment populations are moved as a single unit, this precludes the necessity to track disease group age because passage between groups becomes an inherent feature of transcending vectors. Thus a partially-immune animal will pass daily towards (and eventually through) susceptibility without the need to track group age. Separate vectors are required for recovered and vaccinally-immune individuals, since these groups exhibit differing rates of waning antibody. Individuals incubating the disease do not initially excrete virus and thus infected individuals enter the right-hand side of the virus matrix, passing horizontally to the left (through the incubation matrix). The incubation period can be shortened as the infection becomes more acute. Finally, as infected individuals reach the far left-hand column of the virus matrix (the challenge vector), they begin to shed virus and this reaches a peak. Levels of virus excretion then decrease as the infected individuals descend the challenge vector, one or more segments per time period (usually days). Eventually they move from the base of the challenge vector to the top of the recovered vector.

1.34. Determination of the Vector Transitions

Movement of the individuals within the vectors is achieved by regular increment/decrement of the respective vector segment populations. Inter-vector transitions can effectively be reduced to the following:

i. Affected individuals that reach the base of the challenge vector and pass directly into the top of the recovered vector;
ii. Recovered individuals that pass as susceptibles from the base of the recovered vector, to the base of the vaccinal loss vector, and
iii. Infected susceptibles/partially-immune that pass from the vaccinal loss/vaccinal boost vectors to the virus matrix through successful challenge.

Transitions (i) and (ii) occur within a single time period, and require a simple decrement/ increment of the appropriate segment populations. Type (iii) transitions may be determined as follows:

1. The relationship between a successful viral challenge and a susceptible or partially-immune individual's protecting antibody titre is a linear one. [In Figure 13 the titre levels of $100/r_1$ to $45/r_1$ have been designated as threshold values.]
2. Below a protecting level of $45/r_1$ a susceptible individual will succumb to any level of challenge and above a protecting level of

$100/r_1$ an immune animal is not infected. Whilst the virus matrix is subdivided into an incubation period matrix and a challenge vector, the challenge vector is further divided down its length into x segments of descending viral output, with an equal difference in challenge level between the segments - the greatest excretion level is from segment x at the top of the challenge vector. Those individuals on the antibody vector with a titre below x_i/x_{tot} * $100/r_1$ (where x_i = the segment number of the challenge, and x_{tot} = the total number of segments in the challenge vector) will succumb to the challenge, whilst those above this level will not.

3. Challenged individuals with antibody titre just below the protection level pass to the bottom of the incubation matrix, and those at the base of the antibody vectors pass into the same row of the incubation matrix as the challenge source (Figure 13). Individuals in between these antibody levels similarly pass into respective incubation matrix segments, with those of high titre levels entering the lower segments and vice versa. Thus, by cross matching the transitions from the antibody vectors to incubation matrix, the following in vivo observations are modelled:

   a. High challenge on a susceptible produces acute infection,
   b. Successful challenge on a partially-immune animal produces mild infection, and
   c. Low challenge on a susceptible will also give mild infection because the individuals at the base of the antibody vectors will still pass into a low segment of the incubation matrix.

Epidemiology is essentially a stochastic process, and the implementation of a stochastic selection for challenge serves to enhance the epidemiological realism of the model. Hence, each individual in the challenge vector is taken in turn, to challenge one or more individuals (chosen at random) from the combined populations of the two antibody vectors. The outcome of each challenge is determined by the challenge level and the antibody protection of the challenged individual (described above).

The number of challenges made by each animal in the challenge vector is given by a dynamic contact rate (CR).

1.35. Dynamic Contact Rate

The infected percentage of a population during an outbreak is usually low in comparison to the population size, and thus the implementation of a dynamic CR does not exert a high processing load at runtime. Dynamic CR is achieved by assigning a variable integer CR over several time intervals (or between several infected individuals), rather than an average static CR for one infected animal per time interval. Dynamic CR includes the possible repeat selection of uninfected individuals for one time period, and this is reflected in the challenge process described above. Mobility of the challenge individuals(s) will not influence CR since the uninfected individuals possess 100% mobility - a diseased animal is just as likely to meet mobile uninfected individuals, whether it is mobile or immobile itself.

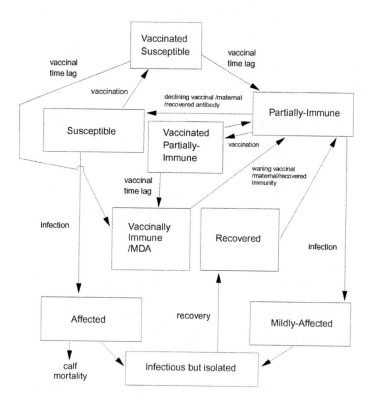

Figure 14. Flow diagram showing additional disease groups.

1.36. Vaccinal Boost

Vaccine administration during the course of a scenario necessitates lateral transfer of segment populations from the vaccinal loss vector to the equivalent vaccinal boost vector segments. The percentage transfer is governed by the proportion of age group individuals that are vaccinated. The default is 100%. For the period of vaccinal boost the segment populations ascend the vaccinal boost vector *en bloc*, limited only by the top of the vector, and at the end of which, they pass back laterally to the corresponding segment on the vaccinal loss vector.

1.37. Disease Group Populations at Time t_0

The majority of a population (at time t_0) enters the partially-immune or susceptible disease groups. The proportions of this division however, are potentially prone to error and the difficulty lies in both defining each group, and accounting for the variability of pre-outbreak vaccination programmes. Partially-immune individuals can be defined as those with an antibody titre falling within a pre-determined range. Unvaccinated populations can generally be given zero values for immunity. Where a population has a history of vaccinal control, the level of antibody (following vaccination) must be quantified with respect to time in order to extrapolate the current antibody levels. Finally, whilst population sampling may provide some indication as to past or present antibody titres, the mechanism for extrapolating future changes in titre has to be precise, since frequent sampling may be neither economic nor practical.

Vectors inherently lend themselves to accommodating the above requirements in the following ways:

i.   Titre variance within a population group is binomially distributed down the length of the vectors. This is because during the course of an outbreak, the variance between group individuals remains notably constant through time (Figure 15).

ii. T_{max} (Figure 13) represents the maximal titre value attainable after vaccination with 100% efficiency, and is assigned to the top of the vaccinal vectors. Tv is the maximal modal titre after vaccination: this may be a fraction of T_{max}, dependent upon the efficiency of the vaccine used. For unvaccinated populations, Tv is assumed to be zero, and for scenarios that lack a full vaccinal history, Tv is assigned the value of T_{max}.

iii. Tto is the modal titre value of the age group at day zero of the scenario, and is calculated by descent of the vector from Tv. The descent is dependent upon both the titre half-life and the time period since previous vaccination. The variance described in (i) above is subsequently applied down the vaccinal loss vector around Tto. For vaccinated populations the accuracy of the distribution within the antibody vectors is dependent upon the availability and precision of the vaccinal history. The same assumptions apply to waning MDA in young individuals.

1.38. Partial Vaccination

A benefit from the use of vectors is the ability to partially vaccinate the population without increasing the complexity of the model. Figure 14 shows the extra groups (vaccinated susceptibles and vaccinated partially-immune) that are required using a population matrix, wherever the population or segregated pens are partially vaccinated. Figure 13 illustrates a vaccinal vector used in place of these intermediary states.

The simplicity of the vector model lies in the preclusion of additional disease group interactions, caused by extra groups.

The need for extra groups in the state-transition model stems from the lag time between vaccinal administration and the onset of immunity. Since vaccinated individuals retain their susceptibility during the period of antibody production, they must be modelled separately from unvaccinated individuals. Otherwise, at the onset of vaccinal immunity, there will be no means of differentiating between vaccinated and unvaccinated individuals, and hence, no way of monitoring which individuals become immune. It could be possible to monitor the percentage of susceptibles/ partially-immune that are vaccinated, and then applying that percentage to the current population of susceptibles/ partially-immune individuals following the lag time. However, the proportion of vaccinated individuals would only remain constant if the vaccinal programme was not staggered over two or more days, and so long as additional administrations were not implemented during the lag time. Since these conditions cannot be guaranteed, the accuracy of the state-transition model may be compromised.

In the vector model vaccinated individuals pass to the vaccinal boost vector, whilst unvaccinated individuals remain within the vaccinal loss vector. Thus partial vaccination of a population is not a difficulty. Where a population is vaccinated entirely, a vector model shows no 'vaccinal advantage' over the population matrix. This is because the intermediary groups become redundant and model complexity is no longer an issue. The redundancy of the intermediary groups arises from a lack of differentiation between vaccinated and unvaccinated susceptibles, since the entire population will have been vaccinated. Nevertheless, partial vaccination of a population is still an important consideration and should therefore be modelled. Distribution vectors, do not incur the problems of integerisation. The population matrix method retained a stable population size by integerising the transitions between disease groups (rather than the disease group populations), and then counting the disease group populations at the end of a time period. In the vector-transition model, vector segments are predefined with respect to disease status, and individuals falling within each segment are totalled at the close of a time interval. Thus by monitoring the segment populations the disease group sizes can subsequently be deduced. Moreover, since the vector segments hold populations rather than individuals, both real and integer numbers are easily managed and integerisation is not a problem.

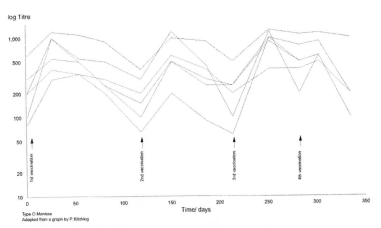

Figure 15. An example of variance in (1 year heifer) titres on a Saudi dairy farm.

1.39. Segregations in the Vector Model

Segregations in the vector transition model are treated in the same way as those in the state transition model. [Methods for calculating ECRs have been described above.]. It is pertinent at this stage to describe the mode of data input used for population segregations. The volume of model input for simulations should be minimal, since an excessive number of parameters may act as a practical deterrent to future field usage. To restrict the number of parameters put into the model at runtime, the spatial topography is outlined by the model user. This is achieved by allowing the user to identify the disease source segregation(s) and labelling them zone #1. Any pens adjacent to zone 1 pens, become zone #2 and so forth, until all pens have been ascribed a zone number. Not only will this method preclude the necessity to input values for irrelevant interactions, but it will also outline the course of disease transmission through the farm. Contact spread is assumed. Zone 1 pens are the disease source at time t_0 with zone 2 pens under challenged from zone 1 pens. Infected zone 2 pens subsequently challenge adjacent zone 3 pens, and so forth until the epidemic has completed its course.

1.40. First Generation Modelling Software

Creating first generation disease models remains relatively straight forward (Figure 16). By using a Visual Basic front end and presenting suitable graphics, it is possible to present an impression of accurate workings within a model.

It also remains straight forward to change the inputs to a model (Figure 17). Altering the internal workings of a model will likewise adjust model output, but these internal changes will remain hidden. The model will then have the ability to mimic the incidence graphs from historic outbreaks and epidemics.

First generation models do not have the ability to accurately predict the future spread of infectious diseases. Nevertheless, first generation models remain useful for teaching purposes, and to observe how different changes to models could affect the incidence and prevalence graphs (Figure 18).

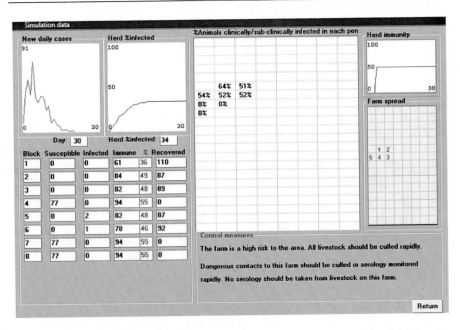

Figure 16. Model output detailing incidence, prevalence, immunity, epidemic/outbreak duration and spatial disease spread.

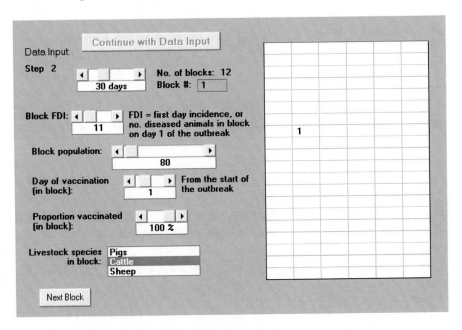

Figure 17. Graphical User Interface (GUI) for data input to model.

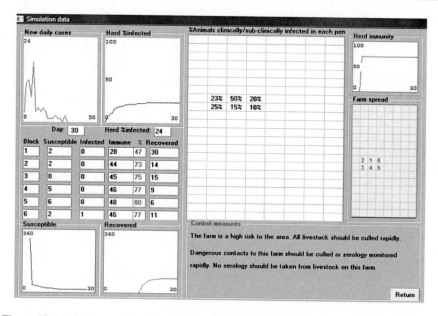

Figure 18. Model output detailing morbidity within segregated sub-populations, susceptibility, recovery levels and indicated control measures.

1.41. The Use of Serological Data

For a model to be of practical field use a validation and sensitivity analysis are required: the former to substantiate the model's reliability, and the latter to identify insignificant model components for removal. When the field data and sensitivity analysis do not concur, then the field data becomes more important and the modelling requires reviewing.

Validation may be achieved by basing the structure of the model and the input parameters around serological data. The outbreak incidence can then be used to verify the model's accuracy. However, this traditional form of validation is based upon comparisons with retrospective field data, and the usefulness of such validation is limited.

Several problems arise in the use of serological data for traditional methods of model validation. These include:

i. For any particular age group, the variance in individual response to vaccination may be large and inconsistent, so as to overshadow any confidence in applying an accurate pwt[] or swt[].

ii. More specifically, where a population has a history of vaccinal control, the level of antibody must be quantified with respect to time in order to calculate the current levels within each segregated group.

iii. Finally, whilst population sampling may provide some indication as to past or present antibody titres, the mechanism for extrapolating future changes in titre has to be precise, since frequent sampling may be neither economic nor practical. In conjunction with input parameters, serological data places the segregated group populations within their respective disease groups at time t_0. For vaccinated populations the accuracy of this distribution is dependent upon the availability and precision of the vaccinal history.

Key concept 5: **Any model can be fitted with multiple factor weightings to enable it (or force it) to retrospectively mirror historical field data. This chapter [1] has outlined the methodology behind such an approach. Useful model validation lies in using an epidemiological model to accurately forecast disease incidence and prevalence [together with epidemic or outbreak duration] at the start of an ongoing epidemic or outbreak.**

Chapter 2 examines the methodology behind developing biomodels to accurately forecast disease incidence and prevalence [as well as epidemic and outbreak duration]. Thereafter, model validation can be successfully achieved.

Second Generation Modelling

2.1. Introduction

One method to circumvent the failings of first generation mathematical disease modelling is to turn the focus of the modelling away from Mathematics and towards Biology. Biology was not designed to be simplistic enough to model purely with mathematics, and pure mathematical modelling of disease spread will probably always remain crude. However, turning modelling towards the biology of any given disease means that models no longer have to be as complex, since numerous components introduce numerous compound errors.

One biological (or biomodel) factor can replace numerous mathematical components within an epidemiological model. More importantly, biomodel factors incorporate the complex series of dynamic interactions that occur between the components of any epidemiological model. Many of these interactions remain unknown and therefore are omitted from purely mathematical models. The solution to improving epidemiological modelling is not to increase the processing power of computers because increased model complexity does not mimic the biology more closely. The more efficient and logical solution is to discover biomodel factors that naturally incorporate large sections of the model. This entails both a closer examination of the disease's biology and a reduced focus upon the use of mathematics. By adopting this approach, the illusive accuracy of epidemiological models can be significantly advanced.

The reason that one zenith of Epidemiology lies in accurately predicting disease spread, is because such predictions will enable disease control administrators to avert the [dire] consequences of a modern day epidemic or outbreak. The secret of predicting an epidemiological future lies in the past, where a given disease has already seeded itself (occultly and undiagnosed) within a susceptible host population: consequently, many individuals will show clinical signs at the beginning of an epidemic. Counter-intuitively, although the number of individuals showing clinical signs at the start of an epidemic [or outbreak] will often be relatively high, the clinical signs exhibited will usually only be mild, or even subclinical. The key facet of this epidemiology is that significant disease transmission has already occurred via subclinical disease. The number of individuals that initially show mild clinical signs then becomes a predicting factor for subclinical disease within a susceptible population and this is directly correlated with final disease prevalence at the end of an epidemic [or outbreak].

As the epidemic grows, individuals with an acute form of a disease will also appear and the number of individuals with acute disease will increase. It is the disease amongst individuals showing acute disease that can be both controlled and abated, using disease controls measures that range from prophylaxis to palliative care. The success of controlling an epidemic lies in targeting disease control amongst susceptible individuals before they exhibit acute disease. The disease challenge against susceptible individuals will continue to grow as an epidemic progresses but an epidemic can be ameliorated by targeting resources towards the control of acute disease within a population.

This chapter examines the development of biomodels, which were identified during attempts to improve the accuracy of ECR. Many progressive steps in methodology can occur when slightly different areas of work or investigation are examined.

2.2. Development of Biomodels: Analysis of Field Data

The idea has previously been discussed of using only model parameters that can be directly measured from the field data, which in turn has questioned the use of R_0 or ECR as model parameters if they could not be measured directly. Hence, an initial analysis of field data was undertaken to reveal epidemiological trends and factors that could be compared to the model structures described in chapter 1. Moreover, this study was intended to highlight consistencies and/or disparities between the theoretically-derived maths model parameters and significant factors from the field data: an accurate maths model would reveal many consistencies and relatively few (if any) disparities. The most appropriate model parameters that were currently in use could thereby be identified. The objective of this study was to obtain a general indication as to the suitability of the model structure outlined in chapter 1.

Key concept 6: **The examination of epidemiological details is not only interesting per se but also provides solutions as to which factors should be incorporated into a model. This methodology led to the identification of biomodel factors, and is equally relevant for a variety of infectious diseases - the methodology can be replicated and then tailored for different diseases.**

2.3. Vaccinal Control: Relevant Factors

The control of various diseases has been achieved for many years through vaccination. Many of the epidemiological characteristics described below are common to scenarios of infectious disease.

Data detailing 20 disease outbreaks has been collated from the field (Figure 19), where the population sizes were large (up to 20,000 individuals) and the durability of the vaccines used was good [providing 81%-98% protection level for 75 days]. However, vaccination consistently failed to prevent the establishment and sometimes persistence of the disease, and this was probably due to both a highly contagious pathogen (producing increased levels of pathogen excretion during an outbreak) as well as the co-habitation of infected/susceptible individuals following diagnosis. Pre-clinical excretion of pathogens (Geering and Forman, 1987) can lead to the infection of additional in-contact susceptibles prior to diagnosis, such that the isolation of clinically infected individuals does not guarantee a removal of infection. Nevertheless, transmission between naturally occurring segregations within a population can be achieved by via contact spread, so the isolation of infectious individuals may still impede disease transmission.

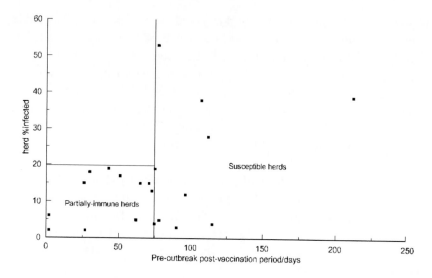

Figure 19. Durability of FMD vaccines used in Saudi Arabia.

No.	Farm	Pre-outbreakVacc	Last Vacc	FirstDisease	PoPv	Herd size	No.affected	%affected	Type	Vacc.Lag	Duration	FDI
1	Al-Zaid	12/07/88		28/09/88	77 days	2050	1081	53	O			
2	Janadria	06/03/88		05/10/88	212 days	160	65	39	O			
3	Al-kharj	12/07/88		20/10/88	100 days	2090	56	3	O			
4	Sanabel	05/10/88		07/12/88	62 days	1424	77	5	O			
5	Ben Amar	25/10/88		16/12/88	51 days	2683	453	17	O			
6	Aziziah	11/10/88	15/01/89	15/01/89	96 days	3747	457	12	O			
7**	Al-Safi	Dec 88/Jan 89	19/03/89	15/03/89	1.5-2.5m	18000	3200	18	O		75 days	1
8	Todhia	14/06/89	25/08/89	25/08/89	71 days	3095***	440	14	O		25 days	1
8a	Todhia	29/07/89	25/08/89	25/08/89	26 days	3095***	440	14	O	7 days	26 days	19
9	Al-Safi	06/12/89		22/02/90	78 days	20000	1029	5	O	7 days	26 days	19
10	Aziziah	15/05/90		11/06/90	27 days	3743	82	2	O			
11	Medyan	15/12/90	19,20/2/91	19/02/91	65 days	2013	312	15	O	7 days	70 days	1
12	Al-Kharj	3-4/03/91		29/06/91	115 days	1885	76	4	O			
13	Al-Kharj	11/08/92	28/09/92	26/09/92	107 days	1845	709	38	A	9 days	33 days	1
14	Ministry	04/06/93		16/08/93	73 days	970	126	13	O			
15	Bandria	13/08/93	01/11/93	27/10/93	75 days	3249	143	4	A	6 days	19 days	13
16	Todhia	15/11/93	07/03/94	07/03/94	112 days	2999	831	28	O	8 days	56 days	37
17	Nakheel	26/07/94	09/10/94	09/10/94	75 days	6852	1274	19	O	6 days		37
17a	Nakheel	27/08/94	09/10/94	09/10/94	43 days	6852	1274	19	O	6 days	99 days	37
18	Al-Safi		09/01/86	07/01/86		12000	265	2	O	4 days	42 days	19
19	Abu Saba	15/11/93	11/02/94	13/02/94	2 days	2609	152	6	O	7 days	54 days	8
20	Al-Kharj	15/11/93	08/03/94	10/03/94	2 days	2303	47	2	O	4 days	42 days	1
21	Al-Safi	19-24/3/94	13-29/4/94	13/04/94		8782	3061	35	O		102 days	67

* adapted from a table devised by Samir M. Hafez
** see Schermbrucker (1989)
*** also recorded as 2895

Figure 20. Details of 20 outbreaks within vaccinated populations.

Many countries have introduced programmes of blanket or targeted vaccination to prevent and control infectious diseases. Despite this, outbreaks and epidemics continue to occur for vaccines that exhibit <100% efficacy. One response to this short-fall in protection may be to examine the vaccination interval. However, whilst too infrequent vaccination can leave portions of the population susceptible to infection, desensitisation to the vaccine could result from too frequent vaccination of the susceptible pool. Alternative solutions may also be examined by investigating the:

i. Efficiency of the vaccines,
ii. Period and level of protection to the population during the post-vaccinal pre-challenge period,
iii. Variability of protection amongst the population resulting from vaccination, indicating any particularly susceptible groups,
iv. Level of challenge mounted against susceptibles at the onset and during an outbreak or epidemic, and
v. Mode or route of transmission through a population.

Figure 20 lists incidence of twenty outbreaks collated from 13 different populations. Each population had a regular vaccinal policy in operation, and entire populations were usually vaccinated within a couple of days of initial diagnosis. The pre-outbreak post-vaccinal period is taken from the date of the last vaccination to the first case of disease. The most recent vaccinal administration will heighten antibody levels beyond any previous immunization levels (Hingley, 1985). The efficiency of the vaccine is calculated reciprocally from the infected percentage of the population, where protection comes from the vaccine, and an unvaccinated population is fully susceptible to disease. This is indicated by the fact that 90% of the outbreaks occurred more than 24 months after a previous outbreak, whilst 100% occurred over 15 months since the last outbreak. Thus any residual antibody within recovered individuals will mostly have waned, and vaccination will be the significant if not the only source of protection. The vaccinal lag is again taken as the interval from vaccine administration to the time of greatest reduction in daily incidence. Vaccinal lag indicates the period of antibody production up to the attainment of immunity (Figure 21), usually coinciding with the first day of incidence reduction.

2.4. Vaccinal Period

In Figure 19 it can be seen that vaccination for this disease keeps the level of population infection below 20% for up to 75 days (or 2.5 months) after the pre-outbreak vaccination. Beyond 75 days the vaccinal protection can rapidly diminish.

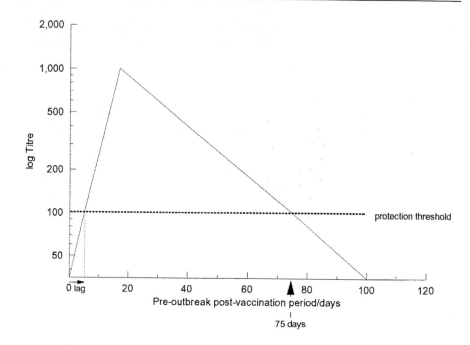

Figure 21. Good response to vaccine.

From Figure 19, an appropriate period between regular vaccinations or the Critical Intervaccination Period (CIP) for this disease would be 2.5 months, since the durability of the vaccines appears to be consistent within that time frame. Moreover, from Figure 23 the level of post-vaccinal protection offered does not appear to be enhanced by a shorter post-vaccinal period: this suggests that between 26 and 75 days (pre-outbreak) post-vaccination, the population antibody titre is held above the immunity threshold (Figure 21) because otherwise shorter post-vaccinal periods would offer higher levels of protection (see T1 and T2, Figure 22). Above the immunity threshold the level of titre would not affect protection. Thus a vaccine given at 75 days before an outbreak may be as efficient as one given at 26 days [for this disease].

A second vaccination (within 75 days before an outbreak) does appear to boost the level of antibody across the population and decrease the overall level of incidence: in Figure 20 the incidence levels for outbreaks 19 and 20 are restricted to below 7% by a second co-incidental vaccination (2 days before the outbreak). Vaccine efficiency with a single pre-outbreak administration falls within the range of 81%-98%. A second pre-outbreak immunization offers an increase in efficiency of up to 13%. To achieve greater population immunity it may be necessary to re-vaccinate more than 3-5 days before an outbreak, since this ensures that the required antibody level for immunity has been reached before a challenge is made (see Figure 21 and the vaccinal lag). Difficulty arises however, in assessing the timing of the 3-5 days before a challenge. This problem could be overcome by vaccinating at intervals shorter than 2.5 months, thereby increasing the likelihood of administering 2 vaccines within the 75 day pre-challenge period. One drawback though in decreasing the administration interval is the increased probability of desensitisation to the vaccine: there is also an additional cost in vaccinating more frequently. In the long-term a shorter administration interval could prove to be counter-productive in terms of reducing disease incidence.

2.5. Post-Outbreak Vaccination

Populations 1-18 in Figure 20 received one post-outbreak vaccination within 1-5 days of the initial disease diagnosis. Thus the effects on incidence in Figure 19 include the impact of a post-outbreak vaccination; this places pre-outbreak vaccination efficiency at best between 81%-98%. The individual contributions of the pre and post outbreak vaccinations to population immunity are unclear. However, if the secondary vaccinations are as efficient as pre-outbreak vaccination, then disease incidence should be reduced to between 0.1% and 4%. There were only two outbreaks (#19 and #20, Figure 20) in which a secondary vaccination had sufficient time to boost population antibody (before a challenge was mounted), and thus achieve near maximal efficiency. In both cases the incidence measured was close to the expected value (of 0.1%-4%). This may indicate that both primary and secondary vaccinations were 81%-98% efficient.

In Figure 19 it is difficult to use the post-outbreak rather than the pre-outbreak vaccination to account for vaccine durability - or more explicitly, to account for the 20% limit on incidence (up to 75 days pre-outbreak post-vaccination) and then a rapid loss of population immunity (after 75 days pre-outbreak post-vaccination). A graph (of good response to vaccine) in Figure 21 can also be drawn using observations from population antibody titres (Figure 15). These include the following:

i.   Vaccinal boost past the protection threshold (Figure 21) is achieved within a few [3-4] days of administration,

ii. Maximal boost from vaccination is achieved within days [15-17] of administration,

iii. There is a maximal titre attained [approximately 1000], and

iv. There is a decay half-life of the antibody [22 days].

[Note that the titre peaks shown in Figure 15 (the first samples after vaccination) are most probably not maximal titres ie. no samples were taken at the 15-17 days post-vaccination, cited in (ii) above. Hence Figures 21 and 15 do not conflict over the time taken to achieve maximal boost.] Figure 21 places the durability of the vaccine at approximately 80 days, whereupon the average population titre falls below the protection level. Eighty days supports the 2.5 months protection period for pre-outbreak vaccination in Figure 19. It can be concluded therefore, that in Figure 19 the vaccines maintained 81%-98% population immunity for 75-80 days (pre-outbreak post-vaccination).

A question does subsequently arise as to the possibility of improving the vaccine efficiency, and several factors (namely vaccinal lag, rate of vaccinal boost and the number of incubator individuals) are considered. These are discussed in turn, below.

2.6. Vaccinal Lag

The vaccinal lag in Figure 24 is kept constant for varying values of the pre-outbreak post-vaccinal period. A variable vaccinal lag should be expected in re-boosting population titre back up to immunity (Figure 22; see lag, from waning titre T_3, and lag, from T_2 of another outbreak). However, vaccinal lag (Figure 24) is kept mostly constant because the variability between lag_3 and lag_2 is maximally only 3 days. A longer vaccinal response time would create higher variability in the vaccinal lag. [The rate of vaccinal boost is discussed more fully below.] A question does arise as to the origin of a post-outbreak vaccinal lag if the average population antibody titre is above immunity (between 26-75 days pre-outbreak post-vaccination for this example): in other words, the post-outbreak vaccination can have little effect on population incidence if the population is already fully protected. However, pre-outbreak vaccination is only 81%-98% efficient and within 26-75 days of pre-outbreak post-vaccination there will still be individuals below the immunity threshold. Moreover, the timing of the post-outbreak vaccination is uniform at 1-2 days after diagnosis. This should create a constant post-outbreak vaccinal lag in protecting the 2%-19% or more of the population that is still susceptible (after the pre-outbreak vaccination). Whilst the detailed parameters (listed above) will differ for different infectious diseases, the generic principles still remain.

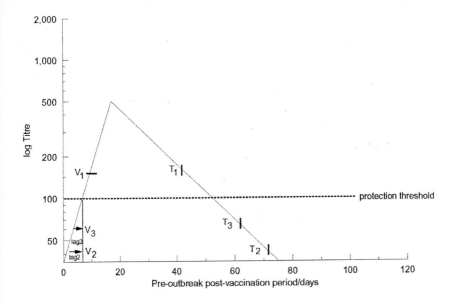

Figure 22. Poor response to vaccine.

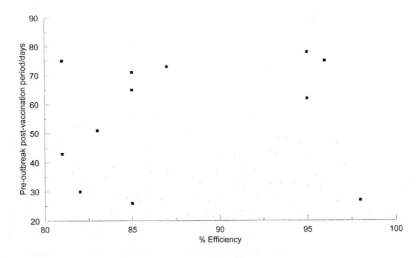

Figure 23. Protective levels of vaccinal immunity maintained for 75 days.

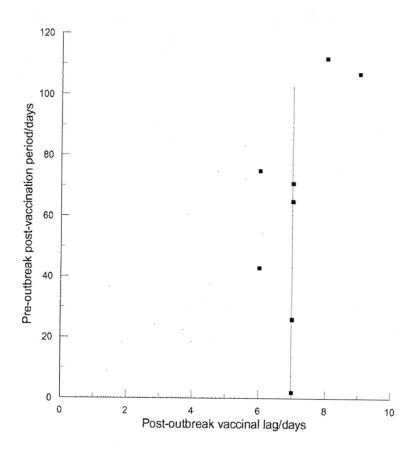

Figure 24. The stability of post-outbreak vaccinal lag.

2.7. Rate of Vaccinal Boost

Outbreaks 19 and 20 (Figure 20) demonstrate the rate of vaccinal boost for the vaccines. Figure 20 shows that outbreaks 19 and 20 have a variable vaccinal lag, and Figure 25 suggests this may be due to a differential rate of vaccinal boost. Unlike outbreaks 1-18, the post-outbreak vaccinal lag is an extension of a 2-day pre-outbreak vaccination, where the population antibody titre is still rising. The challenge (marked in Figure 25) is mounted before the immunity threshold is reached, and the differential rates of vaccinal boost (for outbreaks 19 and 20) are therefore likely to produce different levels of population antibody protection (at the time of challenge). This is probably reflected in the varying percentage of incidence measured for the two outbreaks. Outbreak 19 has the longer vaccinal lag (7 days, compared to 4 days), and thus the higher incidence of infection (6% as opposed to 2%). However, the difference in incidence is small, suggesting that the rates of vaccinal boost for outbreaks 19 and 20 may not be dissimilar. The actual difference in rates of vaccinal boost is 3 days. Hence an additional factor is required to explain the larger than expected difference (in vaccinal boost) and this is discussed below.

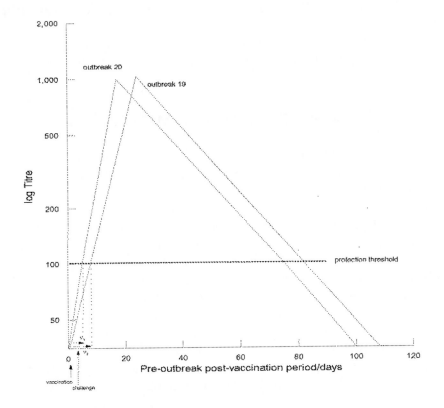

Figure 25. The effect of vaccinal boost rate on vaccinal lag.

2.8. Incubator Individuals

Outbreak 20 has a vaccinal lag that approximates to in vivo studies (of 3-4 days), whilst outbreaks 8,1 1,13,16,17 and 19 have lags that are almost twice as long. The additional factor that could account for these discrepancies is one of infected individuals incubating the disease. Hence, individuals could become infected and incubate the disease before the vaccinal boost can protect them (see challenge in Figure 25). This may be seen in outbreaks 8,11,13,16,17 and 19, that showed population incidence levels of 6%-38%. With incubating individuals exhibiting clinical signs a number of days after the last vaccination, the vaccinal lag could appear to be extended (beyond the expected 3-4 days). Incubator individuals could therefore account for the larger than expected difference in vaccinal lags for outbreaks 19 and 20.

2.9. Successful Immunization

Successful immunization may be due to a low challenge level or an efficient vaccine providing a rapid rate of vaccinal boost. Figure 26 shows a linear relationship between 1/vaccinal lag and the efficiency of the vaccine, where 1/vaccinal lag is indicative of vaccinal boost rate. Thus a vaccine that provides a rapid rate of vaccinal boost for the population, would decrease the number of unprotected population individuals at the time of disease challenge, and the apparent vaccine efficiency (or population percentage that remains disease free during the outbreak) would be heightened. Outbreaks 19 and 20 appear to follow an independent slope to the remainder of the outbreaks, possibly indicating the effect of early vaccination (2 days pre-outbreak rather than 1-2 days post-outbreak) in reducing incubator individuals. An increase in vaccinal boost (or 1/vaccinal lag) shows less improvement in vaccine efficiency (a shallower slope in Figure 26), and this is probably because the early vaccination has already reduced the number of potential 'incubators'.

2.10. Contact Spread

Low environmental humidity limits the likelihood of long distance aerosol transmission and consequently, natural or managed segregations within populations may constitute units for contact spread. Two outbreaks from

Figure 20 (#10 and #12) implicated segregations as units for contact spread. Figure 27 shows the spread of disease within managed populations, and the course of the spread is mapped through the dates of initial incidence for segregations (Figure 29). Interestingly Figure 28 shows a close correlation between the expected path (with contact spread) and the observed path for outbreak #17.

2.11. Nakheel 1994 Outbreak

A number of observations can be made from the field data available on the 1994 Nakheel outbreak and not only do these substantiate a model of contact spread, but they also provide useful details for local disease spread.

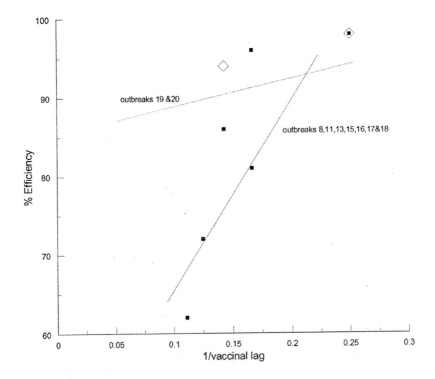

Figure 26. The effect of 'incubators' and vaccinal boost on vaccine efficiency.

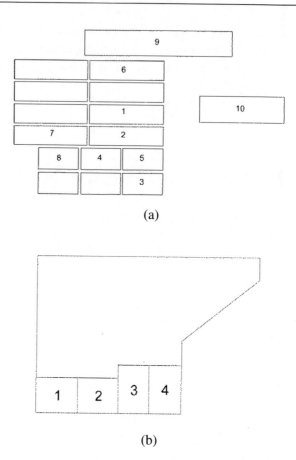

Figure 27. (a) Chronological appearance of disease cases across Al Azziziah farm pens, 1989 outbreak; (b) chronological appearance of disease cases across Al Kharj farm pens, 1991 outbreak.

i.   The initial source pens for the outbreak are pens #7 and #8 (Figure 28). Pens #1 to #4 are close to a road and represent perhaps the most vulnerable area in terms of a disease challenge (Goel, 1990). There is a good probability that individuals in pens #3 and #4 were infected and incubating the disease before their transfer (on 27.8.94) to pens #7 and #8. Hence, although the disease appears in pens #7 and #8 (on 10.10.94) and these seem to be the initial source pens, the outbreak probably began in pens #1 to #4.

ii. *In view of the fact that the period between pen transfer and disease diagnosis was 6 weeks (rather than 3-4 days for incubation), the disease may have been subclinical throughout September. This would allow sufficient time for multiple incubation periods, and for other individuals to become mildly-infected. With the increased excretion of virus from additional infected individuals, more acute cases of the disease would then appear. When the disease is diagnosed on 10.10.94 there are in fact 23 cases in pen #7, and 24 cases in pen #8 within the first 2 days of the outbreak.*

These first indications of subclinical disease were later repeated and noted, as the examination of the available empirical data was extended to other data sets.

iii. The disease spreads west and south from pens #7 and #8, yet a counter-spread appears to originate from pen #23, eastwards (Figures 28 and 29). This tends to suggest that pen #23 is a secondary source pen for the disease, and could have been created by viral contamination from pens #7/#8 at the subclinical stage - perhaps through daily management of the population. The counter-spread substantiates a ripple model of contact spread across the pens (Figure 30). Figure 30 also suggests that the percentage of infected individuals is highest nearer the source of a ripple, and multiple ripples can interact to create higher incidence at their points of conjunction.

iv. Figure 31 indicates that disease transmission slows near the peripheries of a ripple.

v. Pens #20 (block #2), #13 and #4 are chronologically the last to contract the disease (Figure 28). This is evidence for the effectiveness of pen separation in creating a boundary to disease transmission: whereas a ripple of transmission passes from pens #7 and #8 unhindered, transmission is impeded at the boundary (labelled B, Figure 31). Thus spatial separation appears to be an effective mode of slowing or impeding disease transmission.

vi. When transmission does occur across boundary B it is into pen #30 rather than pen #29. There is only a single incidence in pen #30 and more vigorous spread actually commences 4 days later. The single case on 23.10.94 might have been created by a particularly susceptible individual. An alternative explanation is one of rising thermal currents in the hot environment, lifting viral plumes up and over pens adjoining the source; the plumes then descended, one or more pens distance from the source (Woods, 1974).

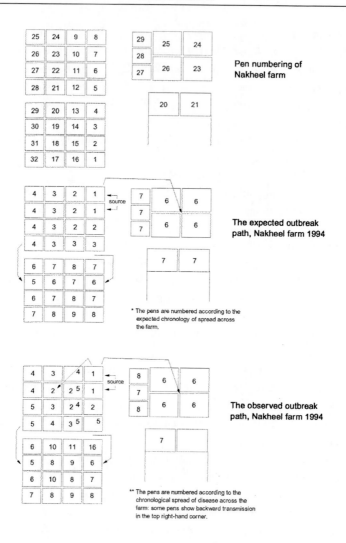

Figure 28. Nakheel farm outbreak 1994.

    vii. An example of thermal lift is probably seen at spatial boundary C in Figure 31. Transmission distance is greater than B (and slightly greater than C since incidence initiates in pens #24 and #25 before spreading to pens #27, #28 and #29). On the evening of 26.10.94 north-east air currents were reported in force across spatial separation C. Following the initial infection of pens #24 and #25, contact ripple spread is apparent across blocks #3 and #4 (Figure 30).

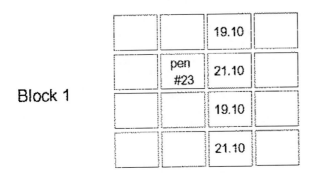

		19.10	
	pen #23	21.10	
		19.10	
		21.10	

Block 1

*backward transmission is temporally distinct from the forward transmission that originated in source pens #7 and #8.

(a)

Block 5 *32		Block 6 *37		Block 7 *37		Block 8 *45	
#5 9 6.11	#6 8 3.11	#7 12 13.11	#8 9 6.11	#9 11 11.11	#10 9 6.11	#11 13 16.11	#12 13 18.11
#4 6 26.10	#3 9 5.11	#2 9 5.11	#1 7 30.10	#16 9 6.11	#15 8 3.11	#14	#13 19 11.12

*accumulative total of ii below for the specified block   Blocks 5-8: 8% infected

**the data given for each pen is as follows:
 i. pen number
 ii. chronological transmission number
 iii. date of first disease

(b)

Figure 29. (a) Backward transmission eastward from source pen #23*; (b) Transmission across cow houses in 1994 Nakheel outbreak**.

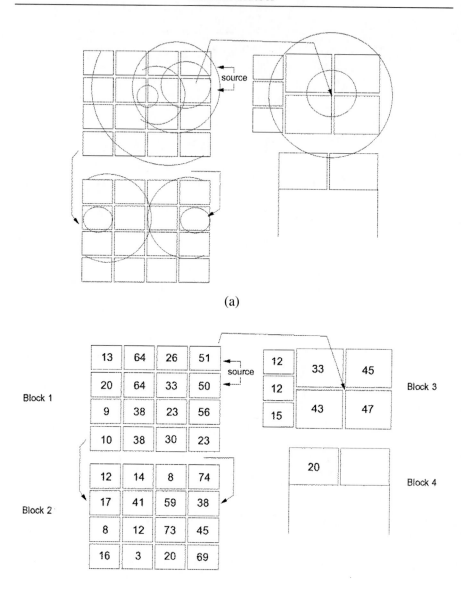

(a)

Pen %infected is shown within each pen

(b)

Figure 30. (a) Ripple model of contact spread across Nakheel farm pens;
(b) high incidence of disease in source pens at lines of conjugation through 'ripple'
spread.

viii. Apart from source point A_1 (pen #30, Figure 31), the only transmission across boundary B is at source point A_2 (pen #3). Pen #3 houses individuals approximately 4 months of age at the time of challenge, and therefore represents a particularly vulnerable area of the farm in terms of susceptibility to disease: 4 month old calves produce low levels of vaccinal antibody whilst also losing maternally-derived antibodies (MDA: Kitching and Salt, 1995). The vulnerability of 4 month old calves is highlighted by the fact that [from (v) above] boundary B appears to form an effective barrier to transmission.

ix. As mentioned in (iii) above, multiple ripples may interact and produce high incidence levels at the points of conjugation. This could be evident in pens #14, #15 and #19 where ripples (sourcing from pens #30 and #3) meet (Figure 30). The fading of incidence levels away from the source but within a ripple, is also indicated in Figure 30: pens #20, #27, #28 and #29 appear to show fading incidence on the peripheries of the ripple across blocks #3 and #4. Pens #5, #25, #27 and #28 (block #1) suggest similar fading although the ripple spread in block #1 is complicated by a possible secondary source pen [#23, see (ii) above]. Block #2 with two possible source pens and interacting ripples, is less conclusive with respect to fading. The line of conjugation down the centre of block #2 appears to limit fading.

x. The entire population was vaccinated on 27.8.94 and again on 9.10.94. With an assumed vaccine durability of 75 days and a vaccine efficiency of 81%-98%, the vaccination on 9.10.94 should have maximally boosted antibody titre before the challenge on 25/26.10.94. Thus the pen incidence in blocks #3 and #4 should expectantly be under 5% (as suggested above, for 81%-98% efficient secondary vaccinations). However, this is not the case. A possible explanation for the higher than expected incidence in blocks #3 and #4 could be an elevated level of viral output with the progression of the continued outbreak (Donaldson and Kitching, 1987). Thus a large viral plume falling on block #3 could overcome the increased level of antibody produced by the secondary vaccination (on 9.10.94). This would in turn suggest that vaccinal control alone for an outbreak, may not be sufficient to halt inter-pen transmission. The idea is substantiated by the fact that the average pen incidence for blocks #2 and #3 are 32% and 28% respectively, whilst for block #1 incidence was similar at 34%.

xi. From (iv) above, spatial barriers do appear to slow or impede transmission. However, from the figures for average pen incidence (Figure 31) spatial barriers appear less effective once the outbreak has progressed, especially for vulnerable or highly susceptible pens (pen #3). The spatial barriers could alternatively have been breached by contamination via personnel.

xii. Figures 32A and 32B list incidence for the 20 outbreaks according to age group segregations locally. The results are summarised in Figure 33. Reproductive status is closely aligned to age and the age groups show differential susceptibility to infection (Goel, 1989). The sample is good in that it is particularly large, whilst vaccination is temporally uniform across the age groups. Figure 33 suggests a correlation between the frequency (see % farms infected in Figure 33) and level (see % infected in Figure 33) of infection within any one age group on a farm. Non-specific, innate immunity and previous vaccinations may also contribute to these differences in immunity between age groups (McCullough and Kihm, 1991; Terpstra et al., 1980). Thus older individuals show low incidence in Figure 33 (or high immunity) by virtue of having had the most recent vaccinations in the population.

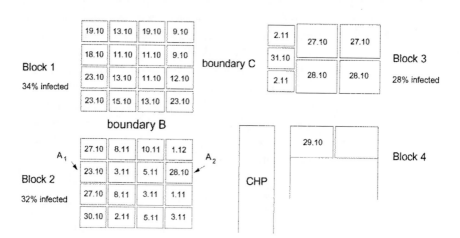

Figure 31. Dates of first incidence for Nakheel farm pens 1994 outbreak.

No.	Farm	< 4 mo.	4-6 mo.	7-16 mo.	in-calf	1st Lact	2nd lact	3rd lact	4th Lact	5th Lact	Dry cows	Bulls
1	Al-Zaid	92	<===	426 ==>	340	315	150	557			158	12
	no.infected	0	<===	426 ==>	340	300	3	0			0	12
2	Janadria	18	3	32	28	24	21	10	9		11	4
	no.infected	0	0	18	25	20	0	0	0		0	4
3	Al-kharj	31	<===	537 ==>	398	300	310	310			180	24
	no.infected	0	<===	11 ==>	1	1	0	0			0	3
4	Sanabel	80	48	380	250	210	182	73	65	50	76	10
	no.infected	0	8	30	29	3	0	0	0	0	0	7
5	Ben Amar	45	<===	634 ==>	471	330	361	242	225		325	20
	no.infected	0	<===	347 ==>	57	40	6	2	0		0	1
6	Aziziah											
	no.infected	0	101	306	4	<======	<======	<======	<======	<======	<======	46 ====>
7**	Al-Safi		<= 54%	infected	===>	<== 1	animal	infected	===>	===>		
	no.infected	3	276	1634	954	114	0	0	0	0	0	0
8	Todhia	62	229	470	551	568	437	309	309		148	12
	no.infected	0	0	25	335	30	22	1	2		4	2
9	Al-Safi											
	no.infected	0	<===	1029 ==>	0	0	0	0	0	0	0	0
10	Aziziah											
	no.infected	0	<===	85 ==>	0	0	0	0	0	0	0	0
11	Medyan	397	<===	438 ==>	146	<======	<======	<======	<======	1024 ==>		8
	no.infected	57	<===	20 ==>	67	79	35	15	4	6		5
12	Al-Kharj	120	<===	<======	650 ==>	375	286	196	111	138		9
	no.infected	0	<===	<======	0 ====>	68	4	1	0	0		2
13	Al-Kharj	39	74	255	272	342	312	207	147	189		8
	no.infected	3	43	54	209	185	80	71	33	31		3
14	Ministry											
	no.infected											
15	Bandria	269	146	498	672	486	298	295	256	320		9
	no.infected	0	3	3	25	43	45	14	5	3		2
16	Todhia	380	176	313	95	564	350	<=====	<=====	736 ==>	385	
	no.infected	13	69	5	14	217	166	<=====	<=====	250 ==>	97	
17	Nakheel	625	<=====	1267 ==>	965	1939	974	<=====	<=====	1082 ==>		
	no.infected	47	<=====	714 ==>	193	122	114	<=====	<=====	84 ==>		
18	Al-Safi											
	no.infected	0	104	170	1	<=====	<=====	<=====	<=====	<=====	<=====	2 ===>
19	Abu-Saba		148	2227	234							
	no.infected		114	35	3							
20	Al-Kharj	259	71	374	298	339	204	627			131	
	no.infected	0	15	4	23	0	4	1			0	
**	Total pop.	2158	<====	6575 ==>	4188	5453	3681	2199	1152	697	898	116
**	No.infected	120	<====	1776 ==>	1335	1029	440	88	40	31	4	41
**	% infected	6%	<====	27% ==>	32%	19%	12%	4%	4%	5%	1%	35%
**	% farms infected	24%	<====	94% ==>	82%	87%	60%	46%	36%	38%	11%	100%

Adapted from a table devised by Samir Hafez.
(#7**) See Shermbrucker (1989)
**Incomplete records and peculiarly vaccinated outbreaks #19 and #20 are omitted.

Figure 32. Listing of numbers affected according to age groups.

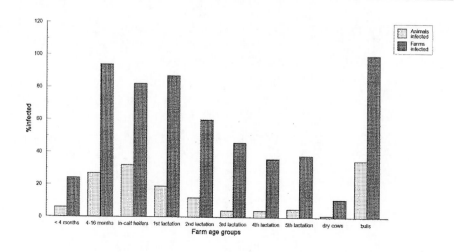

Figure 33. Age group % infected for 20 Saudi outbreaks.

2.12. Conclusions from the Field Data

A number of conclusions are apparent from the field data:

a. The vaccines appeared to be 81%-98% efficient, with

b. An average protection period of 75 days or 2.5 months.

c. Post-outbreak vaccination may protect up to 19% of the population.

d. The more efficient vaccines appear to demonstrate rapid vaccinal boost.

e. A model of contact spread in 'ripples' appears to be applicable for local disease spread, where transmission occurs radially from a source in any direction.

f. Incidence may be greater at source or at the conjugation of two interacting ripples, and diminish or slow with increasing distance from the source of the ripple.

g. Spatial boundaries appear to slow and impede disease transmission between pens, although air currents may carry viral plumes across such boundaries.

h. Disease susceptibility varies within a population according to age and reproductive status.

i. Segregations that hold subpopulations with innate or vaccinal immunity (such as MDA) create protective barriers against disease transmission.

j. Incubator individuals extend the apparent vaccinal lag, and inhibit the effectiveness of post-outbreak vaccinations.

k. Post-outbreak vaccination failed to curtail disease incidence [below 28%] despite a period of 18 days between vaccination and challenge - a large viral plume/ heavy challenge was the likely cause of the vaccination failure within these areas.

l. Age groups show differential susceptibility, and the more susceptible groups not only show a heightened level of infection but also an increased frequency of infection. Innate immunity and recent vaccination programmes may also contribute to these differences in immunity between age groups (McCullough and Kihm, 1991; Terpstra et al., 1990).

Key concept 7: **The empirical data used in this chapter are relevant to the specific disease(s) that were examined. However, the epidemiological analysis (above) is generic and therefore remains relevant to many infectious diseases. The Conclusion details listed above led to the most significant findings in this book (described in section 2.3 below).**

2.13. Biomodel Factors

The population % infected (or herd % infected) in Figure 19 shows no significant correlation with the post-vaccination period. Similarly at first glance, the points on the graph in Figure 34 appear to be scattered randomly, and the scatter graph appears to show no useful correlations that would identify a biomodel factor, nor form a basis for developing a biomodel. However, in Figure 35 it becomes apparent that there are in fact two disparate graphs superimposed upon each other. The first graph relates to individuals with subclinical disease, represented by the blue line. The second graph relates to individuals with acute (rather than subclinical) disease, represented by the red line. Both graphs together provide useful information that can form the basis of an accurate disease biomodel.

Figure 35 outlines the impact of first day incidence (FDI) on the population % infected. A close positive correlation (between FDI and population %infected) is evident for outbreaks with FDI>3; these populations [represented by the blue line] were partially-immune in terms of their vaccinal protection against the disease. Conversely, outbreaks with FDI ≤3 were totally susceptible to the disease and are represented by the red line in Figure 35. A constant FDI for varying degrees of population %infected is evident. A distinction between these two forms of outbreak in Figure 35 could be explained in the following way:

a. Most individuals within the partially-immune populations are protected through vaccination against a disease challenge. Where (a possibly high) challenge does infect one or more individuals within the population, the immunity of the individuals will tend to keep the disease at a subclinical level; as a result, more individuals are likely to become infected before the disease is diagnosed and FDI will probably be high (>3). A value of FDI = 3 has been chosen as the delimiter between susceptible and partially-immune populations. From Figure 35 this will give a positive value (>1%) for population %infected within partially-immune populations. Using the equation for linear relationships [y = mx + c] in Figure 35:

Population %infected = gradient * (FDI) + y intercept

where FDI > 3 and population %infected > 1%.

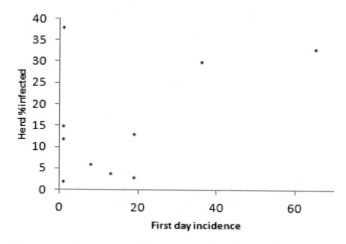

Figure 34. The effect of first day incidence on herd % infected in 10 Saudi FMD outbreaks.

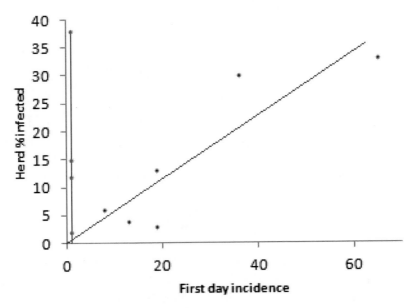

Figure 35. The effect of first day incidence on herd % infected in 10 Saudi FMD outbreaks.

Figure 35 shows that as FDI increases (for partially-immune populations) the disease is more likely to become established before diagnosis, and the final %infected of the population will be high.

b. On the other hand, susceptible populations will contain individuals with lower vaccinal immunity that are likely to exhibit acute clinical signs. Thus at the time of initial diagnosis, it is unlikely that previously subclinical but infected individuals will be present in the population. Hence FDI for the outbreak should be low. In Figure 35 four outbreaks showed FDIs of one despite varying levels of population %infected. For susceptible populations, population %infected is not dependent upon FDI since FDI is constant. It is important to note that the timing of initial diagnosis for partially-immune populations is unlikely to be the start of population infection, because of the subclinical individuals infected before FDI. Thus FDI for partially-immune populations is not necessarily a measure of incidence on the first day of an outbreak, but an indication of infected numbers at the time of initial diagnosis. FDI for susceptible populations is more likely to be a measure of infected individuals on day one of an outbreak.

From Figure 35 FDI is an indicator of outbreak type (susceptible or partially-immune), and the following conclusions can be used to extract model parameters from the field data, and to subsequently use them in Figure 36:

i.   Populations vary in their response to vaccination and exhibit differing levels of vaccinal protection.

ii.   Populations with both low vaccinal titre levels and individuals below the titre threshold of protection, are labelled as susceptible in Figure 35.

iii. Populations with high vaccinal titre levels and some individuals above the titre threshold of protection, are labelled as partially-immune in Figure 35.

iv.   The vaccinal status (either susceptible or partially-immune) of a population is not only indicated by FDI, but is also suggested by the pre-outbreak post vaccination period (PoPv) in Figure 20. Populations with a PoPv period > a threshold value [ie. 75 days for the disease examined in Figure 20] are likely to show a waning average titre level, towards or below the protection threshold. As such, they are likely to become susceptible populations. Conversely populations with a PoPv period ≤ a threshold value [ie. 75 days in Figure 20] are more likely to have maintained an average titre level above protection, and thereby exhibit an immune or partially-immune status. Only populations vaccinated with a vaccine at 100% efficiency would exhibit total immunity to challenge.

v.   The pre-challenge post vaccinal (PcPv) efficiencies show in Figure 36 reflect the high PoPv periods for susceptible populations and the low PoPv periods for partially-immune populations: PcPv is equivalent to PoPv, although an important distinction is described later. The figures of 0.47 and 0.81 respectively (Figure 36) are conservative values for pre-outbreak vaccinal efficiency in the susceptible and partially-immune populations from Figure 19.

vi.   Susceptible populations by definition give rise to acute outbreaks, whilst partially-immune populations give rise to mild outbreaks (Figure 9).

vii. Outbreak #16 in Figure 36 indicates that a partially-immune population may have a PoPv period > a threshold value [ie. 75 days for the disease examined in Figure 20], where the challenge is sufficiently low (or the antibody protection has waned little despite the long PoPv period) to create a mildly-affected outbreak. Similarly, outbreak #11 in Figure 36 indicates that a susceptible population may have a PoPv period ≤ a threshold value [ie. 75 days in Figure 20]; this would occur where the challenge is sufficiently high (or the antibody protection has waned below the protection threshold, despite a short PoPv period), creating an acute outbreak.

viii. The outcome of any challenge upon a vaccinally protected population is quantified by the observed size of FD1. FDI therefore becomes a useful input model parameter, to measure both population vaccinal protection and the level of viral challenge.

ix. The number of susceptible or partially-immune individuals in a population is taken as the population size minus FDI (Figure 36).

x. Post-outbreak vaccination (POV) efficiency is no worse than the conservative value for pre-outbreak vaccination efficiency in (v) above: hence a value of 0.81 is used (Figure 36).

xi. The POV period or day (Figure 36) is not an equivalent of post-vaccinal lag. Post-vaccinal lag measures the period from post-outbreak vaccine administration until the day of the most significant drop in incidence. This indicates the period of vaccinal boost up to immunity. However, the lag is extended due to the continued presence of incubator individuals that inflate incidence as they show clinical signs. Thus the POV period is the post-outbreak day of vaccine administration, plus several days for vaccinal boost up to immunity (ie. 3 days in Figures 21 and 22). POV is a more accurate measure of the post-outbreak vaccinal boost period.

xii. The average incubation period (INCB, in Figure 36) for partially-immune individuals is slightly longer than for susceptibles [ie. 3 days and 2 days respectively].

xiii. The infectious period of infected individuals (ITOES, or 14 days in Figure 36) is measured from the end of incubation (or 1 day from the end) to the loss of clinical signs.

xiv. POV places partially-immune and susceptible individuals into the immune group. Thus, despite any post-outbreak rise in viral challenge, POV maintains the antibody titre of unchallenged individuals above protection.

Outbreak data used to estimate ECRs for partially-immune Saudi herds from intra-herd FMD model

No.*	Farm	%infected	Model output	No. susc.	No. part-Imm	FDI	PcPv effic.	PoV effic.	ECR	POV day	PoPv period	incb	itoes
8	Todhia	14%	14%	0	2876	19	0.81	0.81	4	4	71 days	3	14
15	Bandria	4%	4%	0	3236	13	0.81	0.81	1.3	9	75 days	3	14
16	Todhia	28%	28%	0	2962	37	0.81	0.81	7.5	5	112 days	3	14
18	Al-Safi	2%	2%	0	11981	19	0.81	0.81	2	6		3	14
19	AbuSaba	6%	6%	0	2601	8	0.81	0.81	3.9	2	2 days	3	14

**Outbreak data used to estimate ECRs for susceptible Saudi herds from intra-herd FMD model

No.*	Farm	%infected	Model output	No. susc.	No. part-Imm	FDI	PcPv effic.	PoV effic.	ECR	POV day	PcPv period	incb	itoes
6	Aziziah	12%	12%	3746	0	1	0.47	0.81	10	4	96 days	2	14
11	Medyan	15%	15%	2012	0	1	0.47	0.81	8.7	4	65 days	2	14
13	Al-Kharj	38%	38%	1844	0	1	0.47	0.81	10.9	6	107 days	2	14
20	Al-Kharj	2%	2%	2302	0	1	0.47	0.81	7.7	2	113 days	2	14

** #17 is not included since the first 15 animals are removed by slaughter (Schermbrucker, 1989)

Data used to validate model

No.*	Farm	%infected	Model output	No. susc.	No. part-Imm	FDI	PcPv effic.	PoV effic.	ECR	POV day	PcPv period	incb	itoes
17	Nakheel	19%	21%	0	6815	37	0.81	0.81	8.9	4	75 days	3	14

Data used to simulate the effect of isolating clinically infected animals from the herd in model

No.*	Farm	%infected	Model output	No. susc.	No. part-Imm	FDI	PcPv effic.	PoV effic.	ECR	POV day	PcPv period	incb	itoes
6	Aziziah	12%	3%	3746	0	1	0.47	0.81	10	4	96 days	2	3
11	Medyan	15%	4%	2012	0	1	0.47	0.81	8.7	4	65 days	2	3
13	Al-Kharj	38%	28%	1844	0	1	0.47	0.81	10.9	6	107 days	2	3
20	Al-Kharj	2%	1%	2302	0	1	0.47	0.81	7.7	2	113 days	2	3
8	Todhia	15%	2%	0	2867	19	0.81	0.81	4	4	71 days	3	4
15	Bandria	4%	1%	0	3236	13	0.81	0.81	1.3	9	75 days	3	4
16	Todhia	28%	14%	0	2962	37	0.81	0.81	7.5	5	112 days	3	4
18	Al-Safi	2%	0.4%	0	11981	19	0.81	0.81	2	6		3	4
19	AbuSaba	6%	1%	0	2601	8	0.81	0.81	3.9	2	2 days	3	4

Data used to simulate the effect of isolating clinically infected animals from the herd in model

No.*	Farm	%infected	Model output	No. susc.	No. part-Imm	FDI	PcPv effic.	PoV effic.	ECR	POV day	PcPv period	incb	itoes
17	Nakheel	19%	6%	0	6815	37	0.81	0.81	8.9	4	75 days	3	4

PoPv/PcPv period is not an input parameter for model and no. part-imm = herd size minus FDI

Figure 36. Outbreak data used to calculate ECRs.

2.14. Measuring ECR

Using the above parameters within a state-transition model the effective contact rates (ECR) for outbreaks can be calculated. These ECRs relate to the number of secondary infections that result from one infected animal per time period (rather than throughout the entire outbreak). The calculations for ECR are listed with the input parameters in Figure 36 for both partially-immune populations and susceptible populations.

ECRs are specific to any given model since they are derived by inputting FDI into the model (for partially-immune populations) to produce Figure 37, and by inputting POV into the model (for susceptible populations) to produce Figure 38.

Hence, for partially-immune populations FDI is the measurable derivative of ECR, where both quantify the success of a challenge upon a vaccinally protected population. Whilst ECR is the rate of success per time period, FDI is the initial level of success by day one of an outbreak. The relationship between the two is shown in Figure 39. This calculation for ECR is useful in that it can be used for predictive work in model simulations, and at the start of an outbreak when FDI is known.

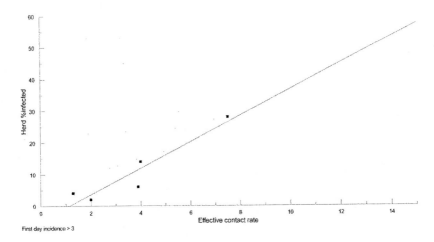

Figure 37.Effective contact rates for partially-immune herds.

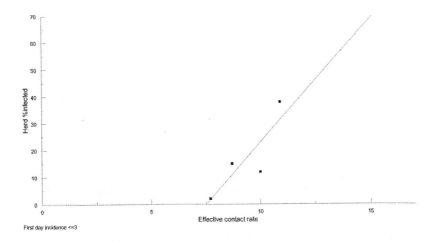

Figure 38. Effective contact rates for susceptible herds.

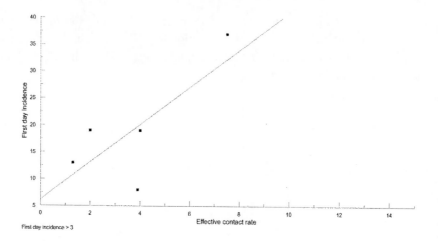

Figure 39. The effect of first day incidence on effective contact rates for partially-immune herds.

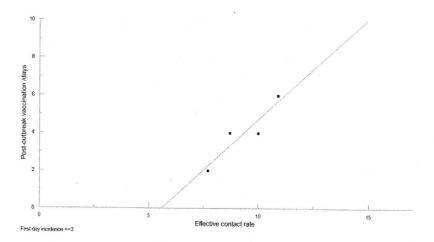

Figure 40. The effect of post-outbreak vaccination on effective contact rates for susceptible herds.

Susceptible populations produce clinically and epidemiologically acute (rather than mild) outbreaks. These outbreaks may or may not be chronic. ECR is usually high, irrespective of the population %infected and a high ECR points to an intense epidemic. Early POV timing is an effective control of population %infected for susceptible populations (Figure 41), but does not have any quantifiable effect upon partially-immune populations.

Moreover, POV can be used as a measurable derivative of ECR from the regression line in Figure 40.

In first generation modelling swt and pwt became immeasurable parameters in that they included a level of challenge against the vaccinally protected population: swt and pwt also included innate, non-specific immunity, and non-specific immunity combined with antibody titre in determining the disease group of an animal (Frenkal et al., 1982). Both the initial challenge level for any given outbreak and non-specific immunity remained difficult to ascertain. Thus the theoretical application of ECR (from CR and swt/pwt) was not easily implemented.

However in second generation modelling, the use of FDI as a model input parameter provides a method of calculating ECR for partially-immune populations, and POV also affords the same opportunity for calculating ECR in susceptible populations.

It may be impractical to measure the respective contributions of swt[r], swt[a] and swt[m] to ECR, in equation xix where swt[r], swt[m] and swt[a] quantify the challenge and protection levels of disease groups within a population. FDI on the other hand, quantifies the challenge and protection of the entire population, and Figure 35 suggests that this latter method produces a reliable ECR for an outbreak. Measuring swt[r], swt[a] and swt[m] offers no improvement in determining ECR. Thus in terms of challenge and population protection, FDI becomes a practical measure for the input parameters CR and swt.

The range of ECRs (1–11) listed in Figure 36 using FDI as a model input parameter, is close to the range (5-13) estimated for CR in the literature (Fraser, 1980; O'Connell et al., 1989; Wierenga, 1984; Wierenga and Metz, 1986; Stricklin et al., 1979; Curtis and Houpt, 1983). The correlation is more significant when considering the fact that CR will be higher than ECR, since the latter excludes unsuccessful contacts.

Dynamic contact rate (DCR) for the vector transition model allows the effective contact rate to change between successive time periods as the viral challenge increases during an outbreak: swt[] (or the PoPv efficiency after challenge) performs a similar function in the state transition model. Following pre-outbreak vaccination, partially-immune and susceptible individuals remain in their respective groups rather than passing to the immune group. Thus at successive post-outbreak time periods a new group of (Nn*(1-swt[])) partially-immune/susceptible individuals becomes open to challenge: see equation (xv), where swt = 1- immunity[s] or 1- swt[]: equation (xv) is independent of POV). Effectively it means that as the disease progresses all population individuals could become infected. This is consistent with the field data since pre-outbreak vaccinal protection will wane and viral challenge may rise as the outbreak progresses.

2.15. Validation

Using the methods described above for calculating ECR, the state-transition model can be tested for accuracy against field data [outbreak #17 Figure 20, Nakheel 1994]. Additional field data could also be used. Figure 36 lists the input parameters and model output for the validation, and the simulation predicts a population %infected within 2% of the observed value. It is important to remember Key Concept 5 (above) in terms of model validation, and the retrospective validation with outbreak #17 is not optimal.

Although the accuracy of this model appears to be good, the output does not map the spread of disease across population segregations (Figure 42). This can be investigated in a more detailed vector transition model that includes population segregations.

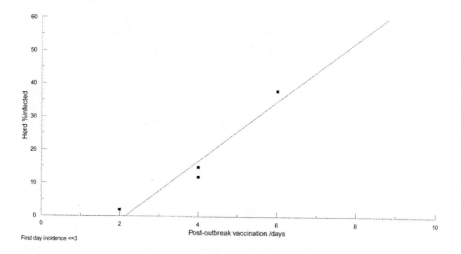

Figure 41. The effect of post-outbreak vaccination on herd % infected for susceptible herds.

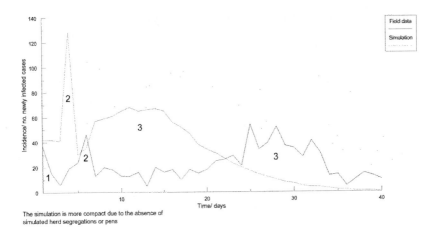

The simulation is more compact due to the absence of
simulated herd segregations or pens

Figure 42. Non-segregated herd simulation of Nakheel 1994 outbreak.

2.16. Summary of Parameters

1. From FDI (Figure 35) entire populations can be defined in terms of their immunity status (susceptible or partially-immune) and a pre-defined pre-outbreak immunity weighting applied: 0.47 for susceptible populations and 0.81 for partially-immune populations (specific to the data sets used). These values are conservative values for vaccine efficiency from Figure 19.

2. ECR is derived from POV for susceptible populations and from FDI for partially-immune populations. This is due to the linear relationships between ECR and POV (for susceptible populations), and ECR and FDI (for partially-immune populations).

3. Other model parameters include: the day of POV effect [calculated by the POV administration day plus several days (3 days) for the boost to immunity], the length of the simulation (in days), population size (Figure 43 shows that for vaccinated stock, population size has no significant effect on population %infected), the period from first infection to the end of clinical signs (14 days: Hugh-Jones and Wright, 1970; Sellers and Forman, 1973), the incubation period (3 days for partially-immune populations and 2 days for susceptible populations), and POV efficiency (0.81, a conservative estimate).

4. The number of host individuals (partially-immune or susceptible) at time t_0, is calculated by the model as population size minus FDI.

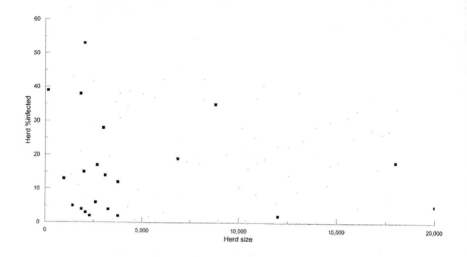

Figure 43. The effect of herd size on herd % infected.

2.17. Model Output

Figure 44 shows runtime input model parameters for a Nakheel 1994 disease outbreak and lists the model output. Figures 45 and 46 outline the same simulation using a stochastic version of the same model.

[In Figure 36 POV is equivalent to the parameter 'Day of post-outbreak vaccination' plus a 3 day lag interval for vaccinal boost to immunity. Hence a POV of 4 is entered as value 1 for 'Day of post-outbreak vaccine administration'. The James-Rossiter Monte-Carlo model gives stochastic limits (to a deterministic simulation): simulations were run 10 times for the Nakheel (1994) outbreak, and the results are listed in Figure 47. As the number of simulation runs is increased the stochastic limits approach their ultimate values.

BBSRC, Pirbright

FMD Model (General) 1.1

Intra-Herd Contact Spread

Press F1, Return to abort program.

Epidemic period/days: **30**
Herd size: **6852**
First day incidence: **37**
Day of post-outbreak vaccine administration: 1
Proportion vaccinated: **1**
Are infecteds removed at diagnosis? Y/N: **N**

Day	Susc	P-Im	Imm	Afft	Maff	NewA	NewM	Inf%	Imm%
1	0	6815	0	0	37	0	62	1	0
2	0	6753	0	0	99	0	62	2	0
3	0	6691	0	0	161	0	61	3	0
4	0	6630	0	0	222	0	220	6	0
5	0	1040	5370	0	442	0	50	7	78
6	0	990	5370	0	492	0	62	8	78
7	0	928	5370	0	554	0	104	10	78
8	0	824	5370	0	658	0	101	11	78
9	0	723	5370	0	759	0	99	13	78
10	0	624	5370	0	858	0	99	14	78
11	0	525	5370	0	957	0	94	15	78
12	0	431	5370	0	1051	0	83	17	78
13	0	346	5370	0	1134	0	74	18	78
14	0	274	5370	0	1208	0	63	19	78
15	0	211	5370	0	1271	0	52	19	78
16	0	159	5469	0	1224	0	38	20	80
17	0	121	5531	0	1200	0	29	20	81
18	0	92	5592	0	1168	0	22	21	82
19	0	70	5812	0	970	0	14	21	85
20	0	56	5862	0	934	0	11	21	86
21	0	45	5924	0	833	0	9	21	86
22	0	36	6028	0	738	0	6	21	88
23	0	30	6129	0	693	0	5	21	89
24	0	25	6228	0	599	0	3	21	91
25	0	22	6327	0	503	0	3	21	92
26	0	19	6421	0	412	0	2	21	94
27	0	17	6504	0	331	0	1	21	95
28	0	16	6578	0	258	0	1	21	96
29	0	15	6641	0	196	0	1	21	97
30	0	14	6693	0	145	0	1	21	98

Figure 44. Input parameters and output for model 1.1 using the Nakheel (1994) outbreak data.

BBSRC, Pirbright

FMD Model 1.1s

Intra-Herd Contact Spread

Press F1, Return to abort program.

Epidemic period/days: **30**
Herd size: **6852**
First day incidence: **37**
Day of post-outbreak vaccine administration: **1**
Proportion vaccinated: **1**
Are infecteds removed at diagnosis? Y/N: **N**

Day	Susc	P-Im	Imm	Afft	Maff	NewA	NewM	Inf%	Imm%
1	0	6815	0	0	37	0	63	1	0
2	0	6752	0	0	100	0	69	2	0
3	0	6683	0	0	169	0	64	3	0
4	0	6619	0	0	233	0	221	7	0
5	0	1037	0	0	454	0	49	7	78
6	0	988	0	0	503	0	58	8	78
7	0	930	0	0	561	0	107	10	78
8	0	823	5361	0	668	0	103	11	78
9	0	720	5361	0	771	0	119	13	78
10	0	601	5361	0	890	0	108	15	78
11	0	493	5361	0	998	0	76	16	78
12	0	417	5361	0	1074	0	67	17	78
13	0	350	5361	0	1141	0	80	18	78
14	0	270	5361	0	1221	0	62	19	78
15	0	208	5361	0	1283	0	53	19	78
16	0	155	5461	0	1236	0	33	20	80
17	0	122	5530	0	1200	0	36	21	81
18	0	86	5594	0	1172	0	22	21	82
19	0	64	5815	0	973	0	12	21	85
20	0	52	5864	0	936	0	8	21	86
21	0	44	5922	0	886	0	7	21	86
22	0	37	6029	0	786	0	7	21	88
23	0	30	6132	0	690	0	1	21	89
24	0	29	6251	0	572	0	3	21	91
25	0	26	6359	0	467	0	5	21	93
26	0	21	6435	0	396	0	2	21	94
27	0	19	6502	0	331	0	0	21	95
28	0	19	6582	0	251	0	0	21	96
29	0	19	6644	0	189	0	2	22	97
30	0	17	6697	0	138	0	1	22	98

Figure 45. Input parameters and an example of output for model 1.1s using the Nakheel (1994) outbreak data.

BBSRC, Pirbright

FMD Model 1.1s

Intra-Herd Contact Spread

Press F1, Return to abort program.

Epidemic period/days: **30**
Herd size: **6852**
First day incidence: **37**
Day of post-outbreak vaccine administration: **1**
Proportion vaccinated: **1**
Are infecteds removed at diagnosis? Y/N: **N**

Day	Susc	P-Im	Imm	Afft	Maff	NewA	NewM	Inf%	Imm%
1	0	6815	0	0	37	0	67	2	0
2	0	6748	0	0	104	0	59	2	0
3	0	6689	0	0	163	0	78	4	0
4	0	6611	0	0	241	0	227	7	0
5	0	1029	0	0	468	0	45	7	78
6	0	984	0	0	513	0	58	8	78
7	0	926	0	0	571	0	109	10	78
8	0	817	5355	0	680	0	104	11	78
9	0	713	5355	0	784	0	91	13	78
10	0	622	5355	0	875	0	101	14	78
11	0	521	5355	0	976	0	101	16	78
12	0	420	5355	0	1077	0	71	17	78
13	0	349	5355	0	1148	0	66	18	78
14	0	283	5355	0	1214	0	69	19	78
15	0	214	5355	0	1283	0	56	20	78
16	0	158	5459	0	1235	0	33	20	80
17	0	125	5518	0	1209	0	31	20	81
18	0	94	5596	0	1162	0	31	21	82
19	0	63	5823	0	966	0	6	21	85
20	0	57	5868	0	927	0	8	21	86
21	0	49	5926	0	877	0	13	21	86
22	0	36	6035	0	781	0	9	21	88
23	0	27	6139	0	686	0	3	21	90
24	0	24	6230	0	598	0	4	22	91
25	0	20	6331	0	501	0	0	22	92
26	0	20	6432	0	400	0	0	22	94
27	0	20	6503	0	329	0	0	22	95
28	0	20	6569	0	263	0	2	22	96
29	0	18	6638	0	196	0	4	22	97
30	0	14	6694	0	144	0	0	22	98

Figure 46. Input parameters and an example of output for model 1.1s using the Nakheel (1994) outbreak data.

No.mild-affected	Average daily incidence.	Herd %infected	Duration/ days
1456	48.5	21%	30 days
1477	49.2	22%	30 days
1461	52.2	21%	28 days
1449	53.7	21%	27 days
1441	43.7	21%	33 days
1449	50	21%	29 days
1474	49.1	22%	30 days
1460	47.1	21%	31 days
1455	46.9	21%	31 days
1476	47.6	22%	31 days

Figure 47. Data from 10 simulation runs of the Nakheel 1994 outbreak.

No.*	Farm	Simulation duration	Outbreak duration	Reduced infection	Simulation duration	POV	FDI	ECR
		Without removal of affected animals		With removal of affected animals				
8	Todhia	36 days	26 days	373	87%	7 days	4	19	4
15	Bandria	25 days	19 days	97	75%	7 days	9	13	1.3
16	Todhia	19 days	56 days	415	50%	13 days	5	37	7.5
18	Al-Safi	26 days	42 days	192	80%	7 days	6	19	2
19	AbuSaba	33 days	54 days	130	83%	5 days	2	8	3.9
Average:		28 days	39 days	241	75%	8 days	5	19	3.7
6	Aziziah	17 days	75 days	337	75%	6 days	4	1	10
11	Medyan	17 days	70 days	221	73%	6 days	4	1	8.7
13	Al-Kharj	11 days	33 days	184	26%	8 days	6	1	10.9
20	Al-Kharj	15 days	42 days	23	50%	4 days	2	1	7.7
Average:		15 days	55 days	191	56%	6 days	4	1	9.3

Figure 48. The duration of outbreaks and the effect of removing clinically infected animals (from the herd) on the level of herd infection.

2.18. Outbreak Duration

The simulations in Figure 47 give an outbreak duration of about 31 days, whereas the Nakheel field data in Figure 20 places duration at 99 days. The simulations are thus short-lived. This is due to population segregations, where segregations slow transmission and lengthen the outbreak: in Figure 48 the simulations are on average, shorter than the observed outbreaks. Duration lengths however, are simulated to be shorter for susceptible populations (with high ECRs) than for partially-immune populations (with lower ECRs). This would be applicable in the state-transition model where there is no barrier to population transmission and the susceptible pool can be exhausted by a high ECR. Conversely, transmission is bottlenecked in the field data by segregated populations, so a high ECR extends the outbreak between and across segregations. Thus the longer outbreaks for susceptible populations are expected. For simulation durations to be accurate there is consequently a need to model segregations.

Figure 49 shows that outbreak duration can be measured from the FDI of partially-immune populations. Outbreak duration is not shown to affect population %infection (Figure 50).

2.19. PoPv Period

PoPv period is a complementary indicator (alongside FDI) of population immunity status. Three out of four outbreaks in Figure 36 (for partially-immune populations) have a PoPv period ≤ 75 days, whereas three out of four outbreaks in Figure 36 (for susceptible populations) have a PcPv period > 75 days. A greater PoPv period can be attributed to susceptible populations, and epidemiologically this can be explained by the waning of vaccinal antibody (below the protection threshold), where the PoPv period has been extended beyond the period of optimal vaccinal protection. Thus susceptible populations have lower population immunity (compared to partially-immune populations) as a direct result of a longer PoPv period.

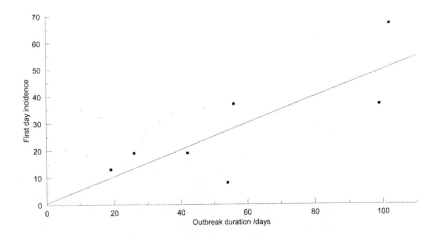

Figure 49. The effect of first day incidence on outbreak duration for partially-immune herds.

This allows a more general rule to be applied to the field data in Figure 19, with partially-immune populations restricting the population %infected for an outbreak to below 20% and susceptible populations not doing so.

Two notable exceptions to the above general rule are seen in outbreaks #16 and #11 of Figure 36. Outbreak #16 occurs within a partially-immune population, yet the population %infected exceeds 20%. Similarly outbreak #11 takes place in a susceptible population that shows a PoPv period below 75 days. The explanation for these exceptions can be found in the level of challenge made against the populations:

i.   Outbreak #16 has a PoPv period > 75 days which would in fact class the population as susceptible. The population appears in Figure 36 as partially-immune due to the FDI value of 37. However, a very low viral challenge on a susceptible population may produce the same initial subclinical infection as a higher challenge would against a partially-immune population: this would produce a FDI >3. Hence, the FDI could have been deceptive and the Todhia population may have been susceptible rather than partially-immune.

ii. Similarly a very high challenge against a partially-immune population could result in one (initial) acute clinical case, and a FDI ≤ 3. Thus the Medyan population in outbreak #11, may well have been partially-immune rather than susceptible. These examples are not the norm however, and the general classification of populations in Figure 36 appears to be the correct one.

2.20. PcPv and ECR

Using parameters (for the state-transition model) outlined above, the functions of both ECR and the immunity weighting (or PcPv efficiency) can be described as below:

i.   PcPv efficiency is a measure of pre-challenge population immunity. POV is imposed on top of this protection, providing vaccinal antibody boost for individuals below the protection threshold at time t_0: this is reflected in the model by the fact that PcPv is applied against Psa and Ppm (the probabilities of a successful challenge), whereas POV is applied to Psi and Ppi (the probabilities of hosts attaining immunity). For partially-immune populations, 2%-19% of the population may remain unprotected after pre-challenge immunization, and these individuals would be the primary target of a post-outbreak vaccination. For susceptible populations up to 53% of the population may be protected by POV, since pre-challenge antibody will have waned to a low level.

ii.   ECR becomes a measure of challenge success during an outbreak. ECR also indicates how successfully the level of viral challenge overcame pre-outbreak population immunity: the fact that an outbreak occurred is evidence of the challenge success. ECR not only encompasses the level of viral challenge against population protection, but also other factors affecting disease transmission such as population segregations, farm topography and the differential vaccinal response of population age groups.

Key concept 8: **Where ECR incorporates a collection of interacting factors, and predictive biomodel factors such as FDI or POV incorporate a collection of interacting factors, then ECR and biomodel factors can effectively become interchangeable.**

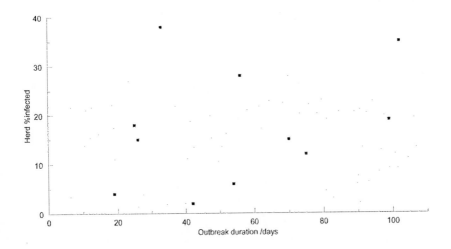

Figure 50. The effect of outbreak duration on herd % infected.

2.21. PcPv and PoPv

The 1994 outbreak in Figure 20 (#21) highlights the distinction between PcPv (pre-challenge post vaccination) and PoPv (pre-outbreak post vaccination). In Figure 51 the PoPv period allows sufficient time for vaccinal boost to both raise the level of population immunity before an outbreak, and curtail any disease incidence that would occur. However, the Figure shows unexpectedly high levels of incidence occurring for 98 days, following a FDI of 67. The high FDI suggests the presence of a large number of incubating individuals at the start of the epidemic. There is no reason to conclude that the efficiency of the vaccine was low. A possible explanation for the outbreak, despite the appropriate timing of the pre-outbreak vaccination, is that the vaccination was not pre-challenge. Thus a high challenge could have been made against population individuals before 19th April 1994, and the levels of incidence were curtailed by the April vaccination but not prevented. Moreover, since infected individuals are not removed from the population, the level of challenge could rise as the outbreak progressed, overcoming the increased population immunity afforded by the April vaccination. There is a distinction therefore between PcPv and PoPv.

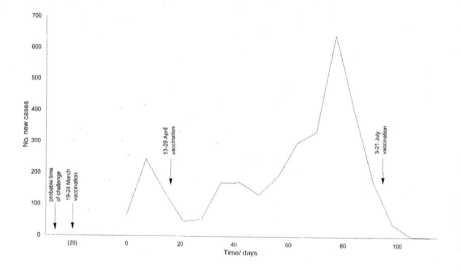

Figure 51. Al Safi 1994 FMD outbreak (young stock).

Whilst PoPv is measurable (as the time from last vaccination to first disease incidence) PcPv is not, since it suggests the exact timing of the challenge. PcPv is measured as the time from the last vaccination (before an outbreak is diagnosed) to the day of first challenge, and could be negative where challenge precedes the last vaccination before the outbreak. However, the Al Safi 1994 epidemic is the only obvious example of this to date. Few vaccinations are coincidently administered between the time of challenge and the diagnosis of first disease. The high FDI (67) points to a partially-immune population and numerous incubating individuals. This was possible because the population was vaccinated at 3 monthly intervals. Thus, excluding the April vaccination (which was probably post-challenge and hence ineffective in preventing an outbreak), the PcPv period would have been approaching 2.5 months. With a long PcPv period the population immunity would be low and therefore the population would be vulnerable to challenge. The April vaccination shortly after challenge may well have raised population immunity sufficiently to curtail the clinical signs of the 67 initial incubators.

Another distinction highlighted by the Al Safi (1994) outbreak is the difference between partially-immune populations giving rise to mild outbreaks, and susceptible populations producing more acute outbreaks. The difference is probably better defined in terms of incubator individuals at the start of an outbreak rather than population %infected. Thus, although Figure 19 suggests that the population %infected for partially-immune populations is usually <20%, Figure 35 demonstrates population %infected levels >20% where the FDI is sufficiently high. Few partially-immune populations however appear to give rise to population %infected >20% and when they do, the PcPv period is approximately 2.5 months, a characteristic of susceptible populations. The populations therefore that show waning immunity and fall somewhere between partially-immune and susceptible status, appear to exhibit characteristics of either group: Al Safi (1994) has a FDI of 67 (partially-immune population), a population %infected of 35% (susceptible population), and a PcPv period of about 2.5 months (either group).

2.22. Use of the Model

A validated or accurate model can be used to simulate a variety of conditions and outbreak scenarios, by adjusting one or more of the input parameters. For example in Figure 36 the ITOES period is decreased from 14 to INCB +1 days. This simulates the removal of infected individuals from the population (on day 1 of the outbreak or at initial diagnosis): a reduced ITOES represents the infectious period from the end of incubation, to post-outbreak diagnosis and removal. The infectious period could be reduced to zero where both incubating and infected individuals are isolated from the population. There is no evidence to suggest that vaccination curtails the infectious period of infected individuals, and a more effective way to protect the population may be to isolate the infectious source.

2.23. Vaccination and Removal of Infected Individuals

In the field data the infected individuals were not removed from the population, although the entire population was usually vaccinated at the start of an outbreak. Figure 36 lists the input parameters and model output of simulations in which infected individuals are isolated. Figures 52 and 53 give graphical representations of the simulations and show a reduction in population %infected with removal. In Figure 48, the removal of infected individuals reduces population %infected irrespective of whether the population has high or low immunity levels.

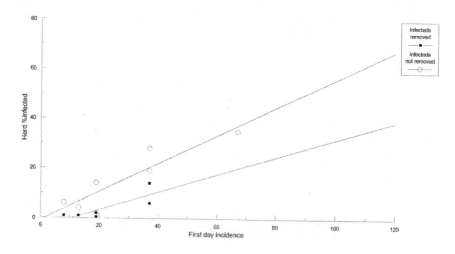

Figure 52. The effect of removing clinically infected animals at diagnosis on herd % infected for partially-immune herds.

Moreover the simulations do not include the removal of subclinically infected or incubator individuals, and this would entail decreasing the value of ITOES down to INCB, at the initial diagnosis of an outbreak. Such modelling is likely to further reduce population infection. A possible reason for the greater reduction in population infection within partially-immune populations (compared to susceptible populations), may lie in the differential FDIs and ECRs. At the start of an outbreak, partially-immune populations have a high FDI (>3) through numerous incubator or subclinically infected individuals. This will maintain the epidemic despite a low average ECR (Figure 48). Thus, removing FDI individuals as they are diagnosed will significantly curtail population infection.

Key concept 9: **Disease spread in susceptible populations is more dependent upon a high ECR, rather than the individual to individual subclinical transmission of partially-immune populations. Hence at the start of an outbreak, removing (sub)clinically affected individuals may not remove any disease source that originates from fomites or inanimate origins, and population infection may only be reduced to a lesser degree.**

The high ECRs of susceptible populations are produced by low PcPv efficiency, long PoPv periods and waning vaccinal antibody. In conclusion, simulations in Figure 48 suggest that both partially-immune and susceptible populations are significantly protected by the removal of disease sources.

It is important to note that whilst the isolation of infected individuals will decrease the population %infected, it will not decrease the predictive value of the biomodel factors FDI and POV.

In partially-immune populations, FDI is a measure of seeded subclinical disease prior to diagnosis. Hence, within partially-immune populations it is not possible to isolate infected individuals prior to the start of an outbreak, and FDI remains a predictive biomodel factor for subclinical disease. Figure 52 indicates that isolating infected individuals will decrease population %infected because transmission continues beyond initial diagnosis.

Within susceptible populations, the predictive value of POV is maintained in Figure 53 when infected individuals are isolated and the population %infected is reduced. The failure to isolate infected individuals represents an informative worst case scenario for disease control administrators.

It is also important to note that the speed of disease control is less important for partially-immune populations where transmission rates are significantly slower compared to totally susceptible populations.

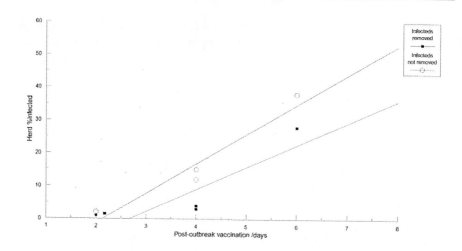

Figure 53. The effect of removing clinically infected animals at diagnosis on herd % infected for susceptible herds.

2.24. Multiple Vaccinations

Only vaccines of 100% efficiency guarantee full population protection against a disease challenge. Figure 19 indicates that the vaccines in the presented field data had been 81%-98% efficient in the past, presenting the possibility of renewed outbreaks in the future. Reducing the time interval between vaccinations should raise population immunity towards full protection, and theoretically two pre-outbreak vaccinations would offer 96%-99.9% population immunity. This idea is supported by outbreaks #19 and #20 (Figure 20), in which the populations received a second pre-outbreak vaccination shortly before a challenge was mounted. Both outbreaks showed reduced population %infected levels (2% and 6% respectively) close to the expected range of 0.1%-4%.

A secondary factor however, is apparent in the Nakheel 1994 outbreak. Population immunity appears to be reduced as the outbreak progresses, and this may be due to an elevated viral output from the rising percentage of infected individuals. In Figure 31, block #3 is vaccinated on 26.7.94 and again on 9.10.94. Despite the second vaccination and 23 days for vaccinal boost, the disease spread to block #3 on 27.10.94. Both vaccinations were pre-outbreak for the block, and yet the level of block infection was 28%.

Hence, two pre-outbreak vaccinations within a 75 day interval failed to protect block #3 individuals. It may be reasonable to conclude therefore that against high challenge, multiple population vaccinations (within 2.5 months pre-outbreak) do not necessarily offer an increase in protection over a single vaccination. Coupled with the heightened possibility of desensitisation to vaccine, multiple pre-outbreak vaccinations may prove to be of limited use for some diseases.

Figure 36 lists model input data and output, used to simulate removal of infected individuals from the Nakheel population in the 1994 outbreak. The reduction in population %infected is 13% or 890 individuals in a population of 6,852. Where infectious individuals incubating disease cannot be diagnosed through clinical signs, removal of only the infected individuals that show disease signs will not halt transmission because incubator individuals will still continue to spread the disease.

2.25. Rising Pathogen Challenge

In the field data, pre-outbreak vaccination does not offer full population protection against a rising viral challenge during an outbreak: this is explained by the fact that any successful challenge was initially sufficient to overcome pre-outbreak vaccinal protection, and is likely to continue to rise during the outbreak. Where the level of viral challenge increases during an outbreak, POV may or may not offer protection to the population by raising population immunity: the field data shows that it does offer protection. The additional benefit in boosting immunity that POV offers is less certain for partially-immune populations (Figure 54) than it is for susceptible populations (Figure 41). Susceptible populations will enter an outbreak with generally lower antibody titres than partially-immune populations, and as such more of the population (below the protection threshold) will benefit from a POV boost. Conversely, partially-immune populations will enter an outbreak with higher levels of protection, and be less dependent upon POV to curtail the outbreak. In Figure 36 outbreaks #15 and #18 have the lowest ECR (where ECR is a measure of challenge success) and yet the longest POV periods and the smallest population %infected. Thus, in comparison to the other partially-immune populations, the challenge success is low, and the population %infected is low, but the contribution of POV is also minimal. The Nakheel outbreak in Figure 31 exhibits a FDI of 37 and the population is classed as partially-immune (Figure 35). In Figure 31 POV reduces the block %infected (after its administration on 9.10.94) from 34%, through 32%, to 28% across blocks #1, #2 and #3 respectively. However, the reduction is small and it is the high protection titres of individuals (adjoining block #3), that appear to eventually slow transmission (see Figure 33). The susceptible populations are more dependent upon POV to control the outbreak. In Figure 36 outbreak #13 has the highest POV period, the highest population %infected and the highest challenge success - outbreak #20 has the lowest for all three. From the above observations several conclusions can be drawn with respect to vaccination and population immunity:

i.   Populations protected with vaccines below 100% efficiency may succumb to challenge.
ii. Single pre-outbreak Saudi vaccinations have limited population %infected in outbreaks to below 19% (Figure 19).
iii. Multiple pre-outbreak vaccinations (beyond a single vaccination) may not improve the chances of a population resisting a high viral challenge.
iv. Viral challenge may rise during an outbreak and overcome both pre-outbreak and post-outbreak vaccinal protection.
v.   Removal of infected and incubator individuals from the population curtails disease transmission.
vi. Post-outbreak vaccination curtails disease transmission across susceptible populations, although partially-immune populations may have fewer individuals that benefit from another vaccinal boost.
vii. The size of a vaccinated population does not affect the population %infected.

2.26. Population Protection

From the analysis of the examined field data and in view of the consequent conclusions listed above, several effective measures are listed below for the control of epidemics:

1.   Vaccinating the population at regular intervals, each interval lasting no longer than a critical inter-vaccination period (CIP). In the field data examined the CIP was 2.5 months, and inter-vaccination interval below 2 months did not appear to offer additional protection to the susceptible pool.

2. Use of a vaccine with the greatest possible efficiency, to reduce the number of unprotected population individuals at the time of challenge.

3. Removal of all clinically infected individuals from the population, immediately after diagnosis, and if possible removing incubating individuals from all areas of possible contact with susceptible individuals.

4. Vaccination of the susceptible population as soon as possible after FDI, to immunize the maximum number of unprotected population individuals before they are challenged. The additional vaccinal boost will also heighten population protection against any rising challenge during an outbreak. It is important to note however, that rapid POV is only effective for susceptible individuals and not for subclinically infected individuals within a partially-immune population. In the field data the ratio of susceptible populations to partially-immune populations was 1:1.

5. The provision of a spatial boundary or barrier between individuals within the susceptible pool and infected individuals who may or may not move between geographical locations. It has been pointed out (Hutber and Kitching, 2000) that this could be achieved by erecting a physical barrier around and beyond the managed housing of individuals within a susceptible pool (Figure 55).

6. Where feasible, the most disease resistant age groups should be placed at the vulnerable areas for disease introduction (Figure 33), thereby providing the optimal barrier to an outbreak. For example, disease resistant age groups could be positioned near the approach road to managed premises. Less resistant groups could be situated away from the vulnerable locations.

7. Where post-outbreak vaccination takes a few days (1 or 2) to administer in the larger populations, the most vulnerable groups should be immunized first.

2.27. Sensitivity Analysis on the Nakheel (1994) Outbreak Simulation

A sensitivity analysis of a model re-examines some of the issues raised above. More importantly a sensitivity analysis examines the relative effects of increasing and decreasing the input value of each model component, and observing the subsequent impact upon the model output ie. upon incidence, prevalence or population %infected.

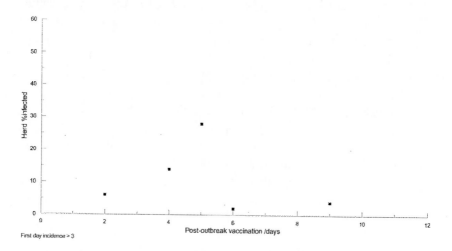

Figure 54. The effect of post-outbreak vaccination on herd % infected for partially-immune herds.

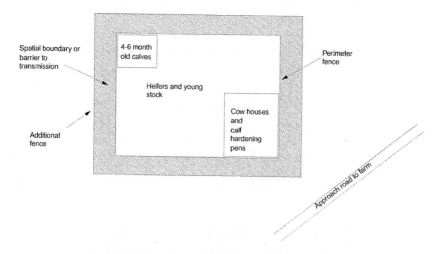

Figure 55. The use of additional parameter fence around the farm and optimal positioning of herd age groups, in the prevention of FMD outbreaks.

In Figure 56 the model output percentage (MOP, or population %infected) is listed, where different model parameters are increased and decreased by 50%.

Figure 56 substantiates the findings of Figure 43 in modelling population size to have little effect upon population %infected for vaccinated groups (de Jong, 1995). Changing FDI exhibits a similarly small effect. This small effect could be rationalised by suggesting that FDI is an indicator of subclinical disease spread, rather than a predominant factor throughout an outbreak. However, such an explanation does not concur with the field data, in that changing FDI is known to significantly affect population %infected, irrespective of the timing of subclinical disease transmission.

Key concept 10: **When the findings of a sensitivity analysis do not concur with the field data, then the field data becomes more important and the modelling requires re-examination.**

ECR, ITOES (simulating infection source removal when decreased) and to a lesser extent POV period are shown to affect population %infected levels: INCB is not altered during the course of the simulation.

An important issue examined by the sensitivity analysis is the effect of POV protection (or vaccination efficiency) upon population %infected. Susceptible populations are more dependent upon POV than partially-immune populations in the control of an outbreak, where PcPv protection levels have waned to lower levels. This is reflected in the greater effect of POV efficiency upon population %infected (Figure 56) compared to PcPv efficiency. The same reasoning also applies to partially-immune populations showing characteristics of susceptibility. However, Figure 19 outlines the greater impact of PcPv efficiency compared to POV efficiency, in restricting partially-immune population infection to <20%. This is not modelled in the state-transition approach and the reasons are outlined below.

The state-transition model applies a PcPv weighting to Psa and Psm, whilst POV vaccinations transfer susceptible and partially-immune individuals to the immune group. Transferring individuals to the immune group precludes future infection, whilst a large weighting to Psa/Psm only delays infection. This modelling is sound in that POV will usually immunize individuals for the length of the outbreak, whereas pre-outbreak vaccination has waned to some degree to allow the outbreak to occur. The modelling however, fails when the level of waning is small (as in partially-immune populations) because a high PcPv weighting will not ultimately curtail the epidemic as it should. One

Marcus Hutber

solution to this problem is to apply a smaller PcPv weighting and subsequently transfer some partially-immune individuals to the immune group. A difficulty arises in estimating an appropriate change in weighting and the number of individuals to transfer. Another approach would be to increase the POV period. This could be justified by the fact that partially-immune individuals may be subclinical and undiagnosed at the start of an outbreak, such that POV is only measured from the time of diagnosis (up to vaccine administration), rather than from the outbreak's first day. Once again however, it would be difficult to calculate the necessary increase in POV (by estimating the difference between outbreak day one and the day of initial diagnosis). An alternative solution lies in the use of the vector-transition model. Vector-transition circumvents this problem by virtue of the fact that it neither incorporates weightings nor is it compartmentalised: hence there is no immune group acting as an absorbing state during the simulation.

Parameter: % of parameter	No. part-imm. value/mop	FDI value/mop	PcPv effic. value/mop	POV effic. value/mop	ECR value/mop	POV day value/mop	incubation value/mop	ITOES value/mop
150%	10,223 20%	56 22%			13.4 23%	6 26%	5 20%	
140%	9,541 20%	52 22%			12.5 22%	6 26%	4 21%	
130%	8,860 20%	48 22%	1 1%	1 3%	11.6 22%	5 23%	4 21%	
120%	8,178 21%	44 21%	0.97 2%	0.97 6%	10.7 22%	5 23%	4 21%	
110%	7,497 21%	41 21%	0.89 17%	0.89 13%	9.8 22%	4 21%	3 21%	
100%	6,815 21%	37 21%	0.81 21%	0.81 21%	8.9 21%	4 21%	3 21%	
90%	6,134 21%	33 21%	0.73 22%	0.73 29%	8.0 21%	4 21%	3 21%	
80%	5,452 22%	30 20%	0.65 23%	0.65 37%	7.1 21%	3 20%	2 23%	
70%	4,771 22%	26 20%	0.57 24%	0.57 45%	6.2 20%	3 20%	2 23%	
60%	4,089 23%	22 20%	0.49 24%	0.49 52%	5.3 19%	2 20%	2 23%	
50%	3,408 23%	19 20%	0.41 25%	0.41 60%	4.5 17%	2 20%	2 23%	1* 6%

* any removal of infecteds is usually only after diagnosis at (incubation + 1) days

Figure 56. Sensitivity analysis of model 1.1f simulating the Nakheel 1994 outbreak.

2.28. Biofactors

Biomodel factors or biofactors are a useful tool to assist administrators in determining when to implement disease control measures, in that they can provide accurate indications of epidemic prevalence and duration (Hutber et al., 1999; Hutber et al., 2006). For example, a lengthy epidemic of high prevalence would encourage the use of vaccines. Biomodels are different from mathematical models in that they use biological parameters [or biofactors] measured directly from the field, rather than mathematical estimates for biological parameters. Examples of biofactors include satellite imagery of climatic conditions to predict topographic disease prevalence (Tatem et al., 2003), and predicting disease prevalence through the distribution of insect vectors (Baylis et al., 1999). Examples of biofactors for infectious disease include first day incidence (FDI) used to predict intra-herd FMD prevalence, and first fortnight incidence (FFI) used to predict focus or epidemic prevalence and duration with respect to inter-herd FMD (Hutber et al., 1999, Hutber et al., 2006). Within the field data (above) accurate predictions are also possible for the successful protection of susceptible individuals through vaccination: again, the field data above showed that for the disease examined, the efficacy of high potency vaccines was 81-98%, and a vaccination schedule ensured re-vaccination every 2.5 months. Beyond this critical inter-vaccinal period (CIP) of 2.5 months, vaccinal efficacy declined, rendering susceptible individuals open to infection (Hutber et al., 1998).

Essentially, biofactors can predict the future of outbreaks and epidemics because they do not dismantle the disease biology in order to substitute it with maths. The predictive capabilities of biofactors stem from regularly monitoring wide-reaching disease factors in a population, such as subclinical disease.

2.29. Summary [Q&As]

Relevant questions have been mooted with respect to biomodels. Namely:

(A) If biomodels are models, and models are maths, and maths should be used cautiously within biology, then what exactly are biomodels?
(B) How are biomodels being used for disease control?

The explanations stem from the different ways in which (1) first generation mathematical disease models are created, compared to the ways in which (2) second generation biomodels are created.

(1) Mathematical (or first generation) disease models divide a population of animals or people, according to their disease states (APRISM ie. affected, partially-immune, recovered, infected, susceptible, mildly-affected). The model subsequently moves individuals between the various disease states, and repeats those movements for each subsequent time period (ie. every day, every week, every two weeks, etc.). The dynamic movement of individuals between disease states

(and every time period) creates a simulation of the epidemic. Some models add locations or relevant topographical maps to the disease spread. The inaccurate guessing of first generation modelling commences for the number of individuals that are moved at each time period, and the first guess puts a numerical value to a theoretical 'Reproductive Rate' (R_0), or an 'Effective Contact Rate' (ECR). R_0 and ECR determine the rate at which individuals pass between some of the disease states (for each new time period). In first generation models R_0 and ECR are mathematical guesses, and are produced from additional multiple guesses about the biology, such as the length of the infectious period for a disease, and the incubation period for a disease, and the level of population immunity against a disease, etc. It would be correct to conclude that this inaccurate guessing is cumulative.

First generation models can mimic what an epidemic looked like in terms of the shape of their (incidence and prevalence) graphs. This becomes possible by manipulating the values of R_0, ECR, the incubation period, infectious period, immunity factors, etc., and if the graphs produced have not created a good match, more 'factors' can be added until a good graphical match is created. [The inclusion of the additional factors can be further rationalised.] It is therefore straight forward to match first generation models to past epidemics. The difficulty for first generation models is to predict what will happen in the future, because models can be manipulated when they have an epidemic to copy, yet without a past epidemic to copy any model manipulations become guesswork.

(2) Biomodels are comprised of few [usually a single] biofactor(s), which can be fed back into an epidemiological biomodel framework – this biomodel framework is not dissimilar to first generation models. Whilst biomodels can create outbreak or epidemic scenarios to simulate past or future events, biofactors are standalone predictive factors. As standalone entities biofactors dispense with disease states, or moving individuals between diseases states, and move towards the end of an outbreak or epidemic where prevalence and duration are measured directly: this is possible because the complex biology has already occurred, so there is no need to guess it. Effectively, the guessing has become redundant. The ability to predict the final number of infected individuals (or population %infected) and likewise

the duration of an outbreak or epidemic, stems from biofactors such as subclinical disease.

Key concept 11: **Following on from key concepts #1, #2, and #3 biomodels contain single factors which are directly measurable from the biology of a disease and hold accurate predictive capabilities. Biomodel factors [or biofactors] are not estimated. Such single factors can be input into biomodels [to calculate ECR] and produce epidemiologically accurate simulations. Biomodels are not dissimilar to first generation models in their structure but they are significantly disparate in terms of the singularity, epidemiological accuracy and predictive capabilities of the biofactor(s) they incorporate and utilise. Neither a sensitivity analysis, nor directly measureable multiple parameters, nor model validation against historical data can become substitutes for a single epidemiological factor that is positively correlated with disease incidence, prevalence and/or duration [for epidemics and outbreaks]. Biofactors remain standalone as predictive factors in terms of incidence, prevalence and duration.**

Section B: Biofactors and Biomodels

Macro epidemiological factors not only provide predictive biofactors for disease incidence, prevalence and population %infected but also determine *where* and *when* disease control measures should be implemented.

Understanding *where* different disease control measures should be implemented, frequently is determined by the historical use of the control measures being considered. Historically, control measures will or will not have been used for specific reasons, largely dependent upon the relative success of those control measures in abating disease spread. Previously successful methods of disease control will normally form the basis of any contingency planning, and will generally only be changed if the macro epidemiological factors change.

For example, prophylaxis against certain diseases may be considered economically expensive to implement, particularly where the control programme is required to cover a significant proportion of the susceptible pool under 'blanket control'. Regions of endemic disease will historically tend to favour prophylaxis since the challenge against susceptible individuals will be high and regular. Conversely, regions that remain disease-free for long periods of time will not tend to favour prophylaxis and its associated costs, particularly due to the low threat of any successful challenge [against the susceptible pool] that might subsequently produce an outbreak or epidemic. Regions of semi-endemic disease, such as those bordering or close to endemic areas, will generally choose an intermediate level of prophylactic protection. Again this is logically sound, since the challenge to susceptible individuals may or may not be successful for any given point in time, and outbreaks or epidemics will only be sporadic.

The choice of *when* to use disease control measures is once again based largely upon economic considerations, although welfare issues will also impact administrative decisions. For notifiable diseases there is a further consideration in terms of [international] movement restrictions for individuals that might carry disease, and similarly regulatory bodies place export bans upon industry products that could transmit disease pathogens or fomites to other susceptible pools.

The question of balancing the economic consequences of disease control against the economic and welfare consequences of disease spread is one that disease control administrators are required to address. Administrators have increasingly turned towards modelling as a resource to aid their decisions, and on occasions some of the first generation modelling inaccuracy has proven to be significantly inadequate. This lack of accuracy in first generation mathematical modelling has led to the development of second generation biomodels and biofactors.

Chapter 3

Directly Measurable Factors - Subclinical Disease

Biofactors provide accurate epidemiological predictors which are available for disease control administrators at the commencement of an epidemic, but most importantly are cheaply and directly measurable within a susceptible population for any given disease. Nevertheless, biofactors remain a useful tool for disease control administrators and not unlike all modelling tools, they are not a replacement for the relevant personnel expertise. Where some biofactors such as FFI are available [at two weeks] after initial disease diagnosis, their role is to assist disease control administrators in the decision making process. Hence the question of whether to change the current disease control measures [implemented according to successful historical disease control programmes], frequently arises several weeks into an epidemic. Consequently, the use of biofactors such as FFI become a timely tool to use in assessing whether a change in the disease control measures would be productive in abating disease spread, or counterproductive.

Key concept 12: **Where biofactors incorporate the heterogeneity of the relevant epidemiology for a given disease, they remain mechanistic because the quantitative predictive value of any given biofactor is not impacted by the incorporated heterogeneity: the heterogeneity predetermines the biofactor's quantitative value, but this predetermination also temporally precedes the calculation of the correlated predicted parameter, and as such the heterogeneity does not determine the value of the correlated predicted parameter. Disease diagnosis and a** subsequent implementation of control measures represent the temporal delimiter between any previous epidemiological heterogeneity and an epidemiological prediction using the biofactor – control measures halt the previous spread of disease at the concurrent point of the biofactor prediction.

Hence the biofactor FDI will predict population %infected for a given disease with equal accuracy in humid, temperate conditions as in hot, dry conditions. Similarly the biofactor FFI will predict population %infected with equal accuracy in mixed species populations as in populations with a single host species. Likewise, both FDI and FDI are equally relevant for vaccinated populations as for unvaccinated populations with innate immunity.

The key concept for any given disease lies in finding appropriate biofactors within the epidemiology, not in applying a mathematical sensitivity analysis to maths modelling factors with a range of values that are more phenomenological than mechanistic.

Biofactors and the accompanying development of biomodels represent advancement in epidemiological modelling, and can instil public confidence in the use of modelling as a tool for disease control administrators.

This chapter outlines the impact of subclinical disease in providing biofactors for second generation biomodels, and describes how the complex biology of a disease can become pivotal to its control.

For example, most infectious diseases have a subclinical form that initially does not show clinical signs, and when the signs are exhibited they are usually mild. There is also an acute form of disease, which is exhibited relatively quickly after initial infection. Hence the acute form can be controlled where the disease is diagnosed early, and insufficient time has elapsed for the disease to spread to other individuals or groups of individuals. However, it is the subclinical form which spreads disease without showing clinical signs, and seeds an epidemic (at the regional level) or seeds an outbreak (at the local level). Hence, by measuring the initial level of subclinical disease, it is possible to predict disease prevalence (or the final number of infected individuals): this is because prevalence has already been measured (for past epidemics) at different levels of subclinical disease. There is a high degree of accuracy in predicting disease prevalence from subclinical disease (Figure 35). Epidemiologists have identified similar biofactors in the literature (Baylis et al., 1999; Tatem et al., 2003; etc.). The same principles apply to predicting the duration of an epidemic (or outbreak). Biofactors are mechanistic, quantitative and pragmatic. Historical biofactor correlations with outbreak [or epidemic] prevalence and duration provide a range of predictive values for future outbreaks [or epidemics] - as demonstrated in Figure 35. In Figure 35 the basis for the biofactor FDI is seeded in subclinical disease.

3.1. Subclinical Disease Spread

The principles of subclinical disease transmission are repeated below for this chapter. Subclinical disease spreads before the clinical signs are shown, so when the signs are eventually shown, the prevalence and duration of an epidemic has mostly been predetermined. The control of disease spread still remains possible for individuals that have not become infected with subclinical disease. By measuring the level of subclinical disease it is possible to both predict prevalence and duration, and *in real time simulate what will happen during an epidemic before it has happened.* This is again possible because the disease has already spread but the clinical signs have not yet appeared. It is biofactors [such as the subclinical disease factors FDI and FFI] which can be incorporated into biomodels to quantify R_0 or ECR - this allows model simulations to test whether certain disease control measures or contingency plans would be effective in the future, or could abate any given outbreak or epidemic.

3.2. Contingency Planning

Re-examination of the biology often provides a fascinating (and unseen) outcome, around which some accurate and simple biomodels can be built; moreover, any contingency plans for disease control should be formed during the time periods between epidemics. Many infectious diseases (both viral and bacterial) exhibit similar epidemiological characteristics that will yield biofactors and build accurate biomodels, and these can determine *how*, *when* and *where* a disease will spread. Some diseases are of significant economic importance such as BSE and Foot-and-Mouth Disease. Other transboundary and emerging diseases hold significance for both animals and people alike, or hold the potential for creating worldwide pandemics, such as SARS, Avian Flu, Swine Flu, etc. All of these diseases exhibit subclinical and acute forms.

Monitoring subclinical disease as a predictor for the scale of an epidemic means that the public can be reassured where an epidemic has a low threat to human (or individual) health, and administrators can provide accurate warnings whenever the threat becomes high. Subclinical disease is exhibited by most viral and bacterial diseases, and is therefore a universal predictor for the future scale of a given epidemic or outbreak at the commencement of an epidemic or outbreak. Similarly pandemics can be controlled by monitoring subclinical disease as it spreads its regional foci across international populations.

3.3. Source of Infection

It is important to remove the source of infection from within a population, since this will affect the challenge level during an outbreak. Identifying the disease source is not always simple, especially where the disease has originated from subclinically infected individuals. Moreover, populations with subclinical disease frequently show secondary sources of origin, which can prove elusive during the tracing of disease spread and consequently hinder the success of implemented control measures. A method that can be employed to trace subclinical disease (SCD) within a population is to map the source foci through monitoring first, second and third-day incidence. By definition these biofactors measure the disease incidence on the first, second and third days of an outbreak, following initial diagnosis of infection.

3.4. Identifying Subclinical Disease

For disease control purposes it is beneficial that first (FDI), second (SDI) and third-day (TDI) incidence can be measured at the onset of an outbreak. Clearly, each focus will present its own FDI, SDI and TDI.

The red line in Figure 57 shows that for susceptible populations with waning immunological protection (vaccinal or innate immunity) and with individuals exhibiting acute clinical signs:

1.   FDI is low
2.   SDI is low
3.   TDI is low.

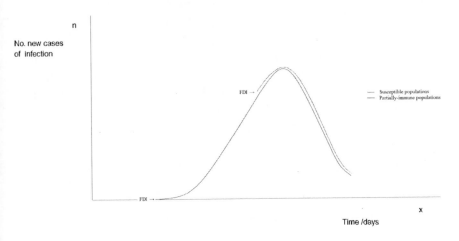

Figure 57. Disease incidence for susceptible and partially-immune populations.

The incidence graphs for susceptible populations will be bell-shaped.
The black line in Figure 57 shows that for partially-immune populations with protection (vaccinal or innate immunity) just below or above the protective threshold, and with individuals exhibiting mild clinical signs:

1. FDI is high
2. SDI is high
3. TDI is high.

The incidence graphs for partially-immune populations will be partially bell-shaped, where the initial section of the bell-shape is absent due to occult subclinical disease spread.

3.5. Differential Control

a. For partially-immune populations exhibiting SCD the speed of disease control is not critical due to the slow transmission rate and the fact that occult transmission has already occurred. It is nevertheless important to abate disease spread, since the increasing level of pathogen excretion from infectious individuals will heighten disease challenge made against in-contact susceptibles, either locally or at a distance (via aerosol transmission, movement of individuals, etc.).

Since the disease has spread occultly with SCD prior to initial diagnosis, there will be a requirement to widen the surveillance zones around newly infected cases, both geographically and temporally. Monitoring individuals through blood sampling and serological testing will reveal the extent of infected cases. False-positive and false-negative results are encountered where the disease diagnosis has been based upon clinical signs. For example, during the 2001 UK foot-and-mouth disease epidemic, a flock of sheep was corralled for blood sampling and serological testing. There was an absence of specific clinical signs although during corralling pyrexia was noted throughout the flock. The serology proved to negative [with zero cases of infected individuals] and the exhibited pyrexia was due to the exertions of corralling.

However, false-positive and false-negative results are uncommonly reported with serological testing.

b. For susceptible populations the implementation of rapid disease control measures is important, since without occult SCD transmission most of the population can be protected against infection (through vaccination) or protected from the infection source (by isolating the latter).

3.6. Carriers

The transmission of disease through carrier individuals has been discussed in the literature, where carriers are usually recovered individuals that continue to excrete pathogenic material but do not exhibit clinical signs of infection. Carriers are similar to individuals with SCD in that they remain infectious but subclinical.

Whilst SCD transmission in some species is slow (Kitching and Hughes, 2002) and the transmission of disease from carriers is not always possible to demonstrate experimentally, carrier transmission of disease may occur where multiple carriers challenge one or more susceptible individuals. Hence, where the excretion from carriers becomes cumulative, the challenge can become sufficient to cause clinical disease.

3.7. Disease Challenge

The occurrence of SCD within a population is dependent not only upon the level of protection conferred by vaccinal or innate immunity, but also upon the level of viral challenge mounted by the pathogen source (Hutber, 1997). A high challenge mounted against individuals with high immunity or a low challenge mounted against individuals with low immunity, may both initially produce SCD. High challenges against hosts immediately prior to revaccination, can produce disease transmission that remains occult for multiple weeks (Hutber, 1997).

Whilst it is not currently possible to quantify a challenge level experienced by partially-immune or susceptible populations, it is possible to trace a likely challenge source (from meteorological wind plumes directing aerosol spread, carriage of fomites by personnel, age of lesions of in-contact contagious individuals, identification of infected feedstuffs or contaminated bedding materials, etc.). Tracing the challenge source facilitates the isolation of the challenge source, which in turn facilitates the abatement of disease spread.

The level of pathogen excretion from hosts varies, particularly between host species. Some species may be highly susceptible to a disease but concurrently may excrete low levels of pathogen once infected. Conversely, other host species may be less susceptible whilst excreting large volumes of pathogen during the infectious period (Hutber et al., 2006). The level of subclinical infection during a period of FFI of an epidemic [or alternatively before FDI during an outbreak] significantly determines the degree of virus excretion from an infection source.

3.8. Strain

Where the challenge strain of a pathogen is antigenically different from the vaccinal protection of partially-immune populations, the level of protection afforded by the vaccine is greatly reduced. The reduction in the level of protection is relative to the antigenic difference and can significantly affect the disease prevalence (Hutber et al., 2014). This in turn, impedes the use of vaccines for controlling disease spread.

3.9. Global Changes

An effective approach to controlling globally endemic infectious diseases is to target the geographically semi-endemic regions. To change regional disease status, targeting semi-endemic regions with regular but occasional vaccination programmes will build vaccine efficacy over time. Clearly the objective would be to elevate the regional disease status from semi-endemic to disease-free but there are additional benefits which would accompany the realization of this objective. Firstly in the short-term, there would be reduced difficulties with high challenges made against the susceptible pool, and a decreased likelihood of long duration epidemics. Subsequently in the long-term, the problems associated with SCD would likewise be reduced. SCD is produced as a result of continued blanket prophylactic vaccinations, where a high challenge coincidentally meets individuals with waning immunity. Hence, reducing the abundant prophylaxis from regular and frequent administrations to regular but occasional programmes, reduces the likelihood of encountering SCD. Frequent prophylaxis is not required in semi-endemic regions to combat disease challenges, which remain infrequent and at a low level in terms of pathogen exposure made against susceptible or partially-immune individuals.

In the absence of SCD slow progress can be made in elevating a region from a semi-endemic disease status to disease-free. The improved vaccinal immunity with annual boosters [or for any other increased inter-vaccinal period] may be due to a wider range of vaccinal response, compared to the more regular vaccination programmes: hence within a partially-immune population, the waned immunity levels of most individuals will be boosted back up to the protection thresholds. The immunity levels of individuals are monitored by measuring the antibody titres quantified in sampled serology.

3.10. Macro Epidemiological Biofactors

Examples of macro epidemiological factors (and described above) include:

a. FDI, or first day incidence, measured by the number of clinical cases [or individuals exhibiting clinical signs] at the commencement of the first time period $[t_0]$ of an outbreak;

b. FFI, or first fortnight incidence, measured by the number of infected groups [or premises or segregated populations] during the first fortnight of an epidemic;

c. For populations without SCD, POV or the timing of post-outbreak vaccination (rather than FDI or FFI) can become the means of predicting disease prevalence. POV is measured in units of time (usually days) after the initial appearance of clinical signs within a susceptible population.

Both FDI and FFI are macro epidemiological biofactors which monitor the level of occult subclinical transmission that has occurred within a partially-immune population. FDI (Figure 35) and FFI (Hutber et al., 2005) are correlated with disease prevalence and outbreak / epidemic duration, and as such become predictive biofactors for disease prevalence and outbreak / epidemic duration.

FFI could alternatively be defined as first fortnight prevalence (FFP), where FFP would be dependent upon the first date of infection for a given susceptible pool. However, the date of first infection would have to be estimated and therefore the accuracy of FFP as a biofactor could be questioned.

Populations with low immunity show early signs of clinical disease following a challenge such that initially infected individuals often show acute rather than mild signs. Without SCD infection cannot spread through a susceptible pool before diagnosis, so an early administered POV would be effective in controlling disease spread. Hence an early POV would maintain low disease prevalence, whilst a late POV would yield high prevalence. POV is quantifiable at the start of an outbreak, thereby offering disease control administrators a predictive value for prevalence before the outbreak has progressed temporally.

3.11. Rapid Disease Control

Human error remains a source of inaccuracy for epidemiological models. During the 2001 UK foot-and-mouth disease (FMD) epidemic, significant emphasis was placed upon the rapid culling (within 24 hours of diagnosis) and extensive slaughter (up to 3km surrounding infected premises) of animals, in order to control the spread of disease: some first generation maths models had predicted that the speed of slaughter was essential, and without such a cull,

97% of the national flocks and herds would become infected. This concept proved to be flawed where speed of slaughter was not relevant in 50 per cent of the infected herds (Hutber, 2002). Moreover, 83% of culled herds were disease-free where the 3km contiguous cull of herds around infected premises proved to be unnecessary for the abatement of the epidemic (Kitching et al., 2005).

Key concept 13: **Speed of slaughter (for animals) or the speed of treatment, only applies to the section within a population that does not transmit SCD occultly, irrespective of whether that population is vaccinated or unvaccinated (Honhold et al., 2003). This applies to the many infectious diseases that exhibit a subclinical form. The undetected seeding of disease [that has already taken place before clinical diagnosis is achieved] means that any speed of slaughter is practicably irrelevant for disease control. What remains relevant for subclinical disease is to carefully target and extend the surveillance zones around areas of subclinical infection, in order to monitor the disease that has already spread.**

In areas where only acute disease is found, then the speed of treatment (or slaughter) would affect the control of disease spread.

Chapter 4

A Disease Template

Introduction

Foot-and-Mouth Disease (FMD) has a short incubation period, a rapid transmission rate and a high morbidity level for [susceptible or partially-immune] individuals that are challenged by the pathogen. Such epidemiological characteristics still permit a subclinical form of the disease to be exhibited during FMD outbreaks and epidemics, in addition to the acute clinical disease. As such, FMD becomes a useful disease template to investigate relevant epidemiological characteristics for disease modelling, and to search for appropriate biofactors when creating biomodels of infectious disease spread. Moreover a study of FMD prioritises the epidemiological characteristics that should be considered when constructing models. Some epidemiological findings relevant to disease modelling in general are also included in this chapter, largely for ease of understanding, since failing to understand or review the epidemiology, ultimately means that the modelling becomes an unproductive task. This chapter follows the process of model building for an important disease of livestock.

Key concept 14: **The process of reviewing the relevant epidemiology remains more important than the process of reviewing the mathematics for any given epidemiological model.**

4.1. Biomathematical Modelling of FMD

Models of FMD have traditionally followed two lines of approach, namely one for slaughter control in regions free of FMD, and a second for control by vaccination in areas where FMD is frequently endemic. A possible third approach is possible with the integration of both methods, leading to the development of a universal model for use at the local, regional and national levels. The impact of local management on regional spread is relevant for both slaughter and vaccinal control, and the effect of housing is significant. The timing of pre-emptive slaughter and strategic control are key considerations, together with the possibility of policy changes during the course of an epidemic. Model parameters should be examined for their applicability to variable climatic conditions and differing environments, for their availability in terms of suitable input data and data collation during an epidemic, and for usefulness in predicting the course of an epidemic and highlighting the most effective, rapid and economic modes of disease control.

4.2. Historical Models

During the past decade and earlier, numerous biomathematical models have been proposed for a variety of infectious diseases, and whilst this chapter primarily considers the implications for foot-and-mouth disease many of the concepts and principles of model usage apply equally to other micropopulation diseases (Anderson and May, 1991). Biomathematical modelling remains a comparatively recent or emerging field of study, and progress is inherently aligned to the production of more accurate, more useful and more topical models. A timely and informative model significantly enhances the profile of biomathematical modelling as a useful tool for the control of disease. The provision within the literature of alternative simulations and interpretations increases the probability that accurate modelling will occur, so long as reliance upon any one model is taken cautiously.

Two schools of approach appear to have been established with respect to the early development of epidemiological models. One approach derives various solutions from calculus algorithms, frequently addressing epidemiological issues retrospectively (Anderson and May, 1991; Anderson, 1992; Woolhouse et al., 1996). A second approach uses probabilities to simulate epidemic scenarios and the likely outcome of various control strategies or changing environments (Hugh-J ones, 1976; Morris and Anderson, 1976; James and Rossiter, 1989). Whatever approach is used, an important criterion that remains integral to useful modelling is the applicability of the approach to disease control and eradication. This becomes particularly relevant where the modelled disease is of topical interest, and FMD continues to be the most economically important disease of livestock, as well as one of the most difficult to control.

4.3. Disease Control and Eradication

A question raised by the farming community during the 2001 FMD epidemic in the UK concerned the need for disease eradication and control. Whilst adult animals infected with FMD usually recover from the disease and the prognosis is good for viability or life, production losses are highly significant. Hence, there is little economic benefit in maintaining national herds that become non-productive.

FMD is primarily controlled in two ways: either by a slaughter of infected herds or by prophylactic vaccination of herds at risk in endemic areas. To date, slaughter control has been modelled by inter-herd observations and considerations, usually proposing algorithms for aerosol transmission across geographical regions (Donaldson et al., 1982; Gloster et al., 1981). Conversely, vaccinal control has been modelled largely by consideration of the intra-herd principles involved.

4.4. Slaughter Control

A second question raised by the farming community during the 2001 UK epidemic concerned the existence of a large FMD vaccine bank, held by the Institute for Animal Health, Pirbright. The vaccine bank could be used by bank-member countries (UK, Eire, Finland, Malta, Norway, Sweden, Australia, New Zealand) at the onset of an epidemic. However, slaughter has been the preferred control option for most countries free of FMD, since vaccination leaves the possibility for re-infection after the completion of a vaccination programme and the eradication of clinical disease. The possible re-infection arises from vaccinated animals carrying FMD (Kitching, 1992; Salt, 1993). FMD vaccines are not 100 per cent efficient, such that individuals within challenged but vaccinated herds can become subclinically infected, and therefore excreting virus without being diagnosed. Countries free of FMD and with no vaccinated herds will have a totally susceptible population, and are less likely to accept imports from regions with vaccinal control. Unvaccinated recovered individuals not removed by slaughter, can similarly be carriers for 2 years post-infection (Burrows, 1966).

Cost-benefit analysis models have produced varied results with respect to the economic viability of slaughter compared to vaccinal control: some models have indicated that the cost of replacing culled herds is less than the cost of vaccination plus lost export revenues, whilst other models have economically favoured vaccinal control, particularly in endemic areas (Carpenter and Theime, 1979; Chema, 1975; Dijkhuizen, 1989; Garner and Lack, 1995; Power and Harris, 1973; Thieme, 1982). It could be argued that following the successful control of an epidemic by slaughter, subclinically infected animals (recovered but not culled) may pose a threat to FMD-free regions in the form of exports. Hence, slaughter control, not unlike vaccinal control may carry economic penalties. However, the number of subclinically infected animals is likely to be significantly less than the number of potential carriers created by vaccination programmes, simply because vaccination inherently suppresses clinical signs (Hutber and Kitching, 2000). In turn therefore, slaughter control poses the smaller threat for exports.

4.5. Inter-Herds Models

Many inter-herd models for slaughter control (Donaldson et al., 1982; Gloster et al., 1981; Pech and McIlroy, 1990) have been based upon aerosol transmission. These models are particularly useful in predicting the likely passage of challenging viral plumes in humid (RH>60%), cool, windy environmental conditions, with a high degree of cloud-cover and reduced ultra-violet radiation. Under these circumstances virus particles can survive for long periods and be carried for many miles, infecting farms in the direction of the plume(s) from source. Aerosol transmission is also more significant for outbreaks amongst swine, where the level of viral excretion is optimal, compared to excretion from cattle or sheep. However in warmer, dry, sunnier, still conditions with outbreaks amongst sheep, and to some extent cattle, these aerosol models are less applicable. Under these conditions, a model of contact transmission becomes more relevant, where virus particles are carried between herds by transport of livestock, fomites, and personnel or transport vehicles (Hugh-Jones, 1976).

One possible way of predicting the future course of a FMD epidemic across a region, irrespective of meteorological conditions, lies in the monitoring of first day incidence or FDI (Hutber et al., 1999). FDI is the initial number of animals with clinical signs or lesions, or positive serological results (pointing towards viraemia). FDI provides a mode of assessing the success of a viral challenge against a given farm, and indicates the likely number of infectious animals that have been excreting virus prior to herd slaughter. This in turn monitors the likely subsequent level of challenge against neighbouring farms in a region, whether by aerosol or contact transmission. Theoretically, a high FDI suggests a need for more rapid, extensive culling or the use of a vaccination programme, whilst a low FDI requires less extensive, pre-emptive slaughter. FDI is available at the start of an outbreak, and is indicative of how much virus has reached a given area as the disease spreads across a region. The total susceptibility of herds in FMD-free regions means that FDI will be correlated to herd prevalence (or the final herd percentage infected). FDI thus becomes an applicable, predictive modelling parameter for regions implementing slaughter control.

4.6. Pre-Emptive Slaughter

During the 1967-68 UK epidemic, slaughter control eventually succeeded in controlling inter-herd transmission but perhaps more importantly an outbreak was not encountered within the UK for another 14 years. Prior to 1967, FMD outbreaks had been more regular within the UK. However, it could be argued that the slaughter of infected herds did not adequately control the 1967-68 epidemic until the number of susceptible herds had been reduced, thereby increasing the distance between them, and decreasing the likelihood of both aerosol and contact spread. This argument strengthened the argument for early pre-emptive slaughter during an epidemic. Pre-emptive slaughter works in a similar fashion to ring-vaccination, slaughtering herds around any focus of infection comprising one or more infected farms. The advantage of pre-emptive control is that not only does it remove possible incubating and subclinical animals within an infected region, but it also creates a spatial barrier between the primary source herd and outlying susceptible herds (Moutou and Durand, 1994). Tardy pre-emptive slaughter becomes less effective as the number of infected herds across a region increases; this is because the number of herds required for culling around foci, increases in line with any expanding foci. However, it is equally important to consider the likelihood of over-culling, when clean herds can be slaughtered around a focus if the pre-emptive slaughter is geographically too extensive. Such counter-productive overkill was commonplace during the 2001 UK epidemic where 83% of slaughtered herds were disease-free (Kitching et al., 2004).

4.7. Strategic Control

Whilst the 1967-68 UK epidemic was concentrated more towards the north-west of England, the 2001 UK epidemic rapidly exhibited a geographically diverse spread of outbreaks across the breadth and depth of the UK. Under these circumstances, pre-emptive slaughter around foci alone may be insufficient to control inter-herd transmission, since the possibilities of radial spread from many foci will be greater than that from fewer, more spatially concentrated foci. Concurrent additional control measures may therefore be required and some of these are described below. Such supplementary control measures provide an alternative to simply extending the pre-emptive slaughter: the extended 3km contiguous culling of herds around infected premises (IPs) proved counter-productive in the 2001 UK epidemic (Kitching et al., 2004).

However, for both epidemics the spread of disease across the UK mirrored the spread of FMD within a single herd. The World Reference Laboratory for FMD collates FMD outbreak studies world-wide and holds a large volume of data detailing spread across farms of up to 20,000 animals (Hutber, 1997). Similarities exist between the two UK epidemics and outbreaks for individual herds. Hence, a small number of source units (animals or herds) were initially infected, and this was followed by a period of very few (sometimes zero) units infected. Daily incidence from that point rose steadily to a peak and then declined, as predicted by a SIR model of spread (Anderson and May, 1991). It appears that UK livestock could be modelled as a single herd, with farms acting as units within the national herd. Both aerosol and contact spread (via livestock transport fomites or personnel) provided the means of disease transmission in a seemingly random fashion. Waves of spread were created by spatial barriers between farms, and by natural geographic barriers or other curtailments, such that transmission was periodically but temporarily abated (Sanson, 1992; Hutber and Kitching, 1996). Counter-waves in different directions occurred when re-infection of susceptible units spread back across the same area (Hutber and Kitching, 2000).

The existence of natural and spatial barriers to transmission demonstrates the possibility of strategic control, and could be used when pre-emptive slaughter becomes inadequate. Hence, where geographic bottlenecks are exhibited within an affected region or topographic bottlenecks appear within a farm, these could be exploited to create divisions and sub-units for abating transmission (Hutber and Kitching, 2000). The creation of spatial barriers and hence divisions or isolating zones across a region (or within a farm) may be achieved by the use of animal housing.

4.8. Animal Housing

Models for slaughter control have not to date incorporated the impact of intra-herd control measures implemented by herd management. Such measures (applied within herds not incubating the disease) can protect farms and slow transmission between herds. Tinline (1972) concluded that animal housing would curtail FMD transmission for outbreaks in temperate climates - Tinline's model simulations of the 1967-68 UK epidemic predicted that ring-housing techniques would be more effective for the UK than ring-vaccination programmes.

The implementation of animal housing at strategic points within regional geography or at appropriate bottlenecks within farm topographies, would not only decrease the probability of successful challenges against farm herds, but more importantly would decrease the level of virus leaving farms, excreted by undiagnosed subclinical or incubating animals. Undiagnosed disease and infectious animals prior to slaughter become significant reasons for the continuation of an epidemic, despite the slaughter of infected herds.

The enforcement of animal housing at strategic geographical locations could be combined with an effective use of disinfectants to support pre-emptive slaughter. They could also be used in regions of expanding foci, and in conjunction with pre-emptive slaughter could help curtail the expansion of an epidemic. Zero grazing for housed animals would be another feature in regions of possible challenge, such that susceptible animals are not left at pasture. The use of on-farm dry fodder would ensure that fomites are not introduced to farms through forage materials.

4.9. Farm Management

Disease preventive sanitary measures have been proposed for many years, but their effectiveness is largely dependent upon vigilance applied to implementation at the farm level. Nevertheless, control measures at the farm level represent a source of self-assistance in areas of slaughter control and disseminate some administrative load during the course of an epidemic. In terms of sanitation there should be considerations for the restriction of personnel movement onto and within a farm, and the recurrent disinfection of vehicles, personnel clothing, to the exterior and interior of housing, and to feed coverings (Ondrasovic et al., 1994). Control measures not only minimise the risk of infection reaching a farm, but also reduce the likelihood of carriage across a farm to on-site susceptible animals, and likewise minimise the risk of virus leaving a farm. Further measures to restrict the level of virus excretion leaving farms include the division of animals into as many small, housed groups as possible, with no intermixing of species - large groups permit free intermixing of animals and disease amongst pigs will heighten transmission. The divisions likewise benefit the farmer, in that where separate personnel are assigned to tend units dispersed across a geographically large farm, an outbreak in one unit might not indicate the need to cull the entire farm herd in endemic regions.

Farm buildings that are not used for the housing of susceptible animals have proved to be effective in curtailing FMD challenge (Hutber and Kitching, 2000). Their positioning as physical barriers in the direction of a likely challenge will decrease the probability of herd infection. Using coverings or buildings for the storage of fodder and other feedstuffs, and placing pigs and pregnant individuals (that are particularly susceptible to FMD) in secure housing, and as far as possible from the direction of likely challenge, will further reduce the likelihood of an outbreak.

Another feature of herd management that may minimise the transmission of FMD from wild animals to farmed species and vice versa, is the effective use of doubled fencing, or boundary fencing around holdings. Such a measure provides a spatial barrier, where the effectiveness of the barrier is proportional to its size.

4.10. Vaccination

Vaccinal control is frequently used in areas where FMD is endemic and the prospects of control by slaughter are not good. Vaccination against FMD has been shown to be 81% to 98% efficient with the most efficient vaccines providing the greatest rate of vaccinal boost (Hingley, 1985; Hutber et al., 1998). Whilst an efficacy of 81% to 98% for vaccinated herds is not sufficient to protect a farm against every challenge, it is adequately high to limit outbreaks between farms and to ensure that an epidemic does not spread extensively across a region.

Rapid vaccination following the first diagnosed case on a farm (or post-outbreak vaccination, POV) is as important for disease control as pre-outbreak vaccination (Hutber and Kitching, 1996). Two measurable parameters have proved useful for modelling outbreaks in vaccinated herds. The first of these is POV and is relevant for herds that show a few animals with acute clinical signs at the onset of an outbreak. Waning vaccinal protection in these herds (due to a long period between vaccinations) fails to suppress any clinical signs in challenged animals, and hence these signs are rapidly exhibited when the outbreak begins. Conversely, herds with strong vaccinal protection (due to a short period between vaccinations) suppress clinical signs in initially affected individuals, such that when clinical signs do eventually appear, a high number of animals exhibit them together. First day incidence in these herds is high and the initial clinical signs are mild (Hutber et al., 1999). Both POV and FDI are linearly correlated to prevalence or the final percentage of herd animals that become infected. Hence, together these parameters offer a way of modelling how an outbreak will progress in a vaccinated herd, predicting the final outcome.

An entire herd on a given farm is usually vaccinated by way of suitable protection, due to the small spatial distances involved for possible transmission. A less effective way to use vaccines would be to partially vaccinate herds. There may be an inclination to selectively protect youngstock through vaccination, since young age groups exhibit a higher degree of mortality compared to older animals. However, this would introduce the disadvantages of vaccination in terms of export penalties, without providing the benefit of protecting an entire herd against a highly contagious disease.

The critical inter-vaccination period (CIP) for vaccinated herds is approximately 2.5 months, during which time the average antibody titre is maintained above the required level for protection, but beyond which the titre levels for progressively more animals dip below protection (Hafez, 1990;

Hafez, 1991; Hutber et al., 1998). The length of CIP, together with the timing of a vaccination programme, permits an assessment of the current immune status for any given herd. Immune status is inherently an important parameter in modelling the likely success of a viral challenge against a vaccinated herd. It is also noteworthy that re-vaccination before 2.5 months appears to provide no additional advantage, in terms of reducing the final level of herd infection.

A similarly important parameter in modelling FMD spread within vaccinated herds is r1, the level of appropriate matching between the outbreak strain and the vaccine (Kitching, 1992). r1 should be incorporated into any FMD model including vaccination, since the accuracy of the matching will significantly impact the efficiency of the vaccine.

4.11. Strategic Vaccination

Many countries free of FMD would consider a change of control policy where slaughter had proved ineffective as an epidemic progressed. Hence, the vaccine bank held at Pirbright, Surrey could have been used at some time during the 2001 UK epidemic. The primary advantage of vaccination lies in the prophylactic protection offered to large numbers of susceptible animals. This is in contrast to the remedial action of removing infected or incubating animals by slaughter.

Whilst both intra-herd vaccination (Cleland et al., 1993) and the effect of vaccination on the national herd have been previously modelled, inter-herd spatial modelling for a vaccinal control policy has not to date been extensively considered. Spatial modelling for vaccinations would evaluate the impact on disease spread of selectively and strategically vaccinating a small percentage of susceptible animals within the national herd.

Key concept 15: **It should be emphasised that spatial modelling can also be conducted through biofactors and does not necessitate input from topographical or geographical or simulated host movements or any other parameter involving physical dimensions. Some biofactors overlap into physical dimensions, such as the rainfall mapping used by Baylis to monitor African Horse Sickness. However, spatial modelling, or the spread of disease both temporally and concurrently spatially, can also be modelled by monitoring biofactors such as FFI, FDI, and even POV. Disease spread is mapped according to the level of the biofactor measured at any given spatial location and at any given time interval. Logically it** could be argued that by mapping a biofactor spatially, the biofactor becomes a parameter with a physical dimension. The importance of the biofactor is that it remains standalone in terms of its predictive value and does not introduce any additional parameter(s) that would require quantitative guessing in order to add a spatial layer to the modelling. The fact that a biofactor can be multifaceted, enhances the usefulness of any given biofactor.

A strategic barrier comprising vaccinated farms could be created around outbreak foci, or could be used as an impediment to disease transmission into or out of a geographical region. For example, a band of vaccinated farms across the entrance to a peninsula could curtail spread into or from the area.

A characteristic of vaccination programmes is that they remain in place during the course of an epidemic, acting as continual barriers to disease spread. Hence, areas of vaccinated herds when strategically placed, could divide a region into protected sub-regions, thereby curtailing the spread of disease. Strategic herd vaccinations within a geographic region would significantly reduce the number of herds required to be vaccinated, and spatial modelling could be used to quantify the necessary administrations during an epidemic. The percentage of the national herd that would require vaccination may be low (Hutber et al., 2014).

4.12. Vaccination Combined with Slaughter Control

Where the emergency vaccinations required to control an epidemic are only minimal, these vaccinated animals may be slaughtered after the culling of the last clinical cases during an epidemic. The export ban for regions operating a slaughter policy is 3 months once the epidemic has been abated, whilst the same export ban of 3 months is effective against areas slaughtering both clinical cases and any animals that are vaccinated. Hence, vaccination can be used for control purposes during the course of an epidemic, so long as the vaccinated animals are slaughtered later.

The use of vaccination followed by slaughter may offer benefits in the control of transmission across a geographical region, particularly when the rate of transmission is high and the spread of disease is extensive. During the 2001 UK epidemic, the logistics were not simple for slaughtering animals rapidly and in sufficient numbers to abate transmission, and in extreme cases it took up to 7 days to cull and dispose of carcasses from some infected herds. The advantage of vaccination administration is that it is comparatively rapid, and most herds can receive vaccine within a day. Whilst vaccinal boost in some animals may take 3 or 4 days to reach an immune status (Hutber et al., 1998; Woolhouse and Donaldson, 2001), the most potent vaccines begin to boost antibody titres towards protection shortly after administration. Moreover, vaccines are generally 81% to 98% efficient, and could therefore provide a rapid means of ring or strategic vaccination to curtail an extensive epidemic. The fact that vaccinated animals might be slaughtered after the epidemic has been controlled is no more drastic than slaughter control alone. Perhaps the most important criterion is whether the vaccinal boost times to protective levels, are less than the implementation times for pre-emptive slaughter control. Slaughter controls implemented within or below 3 days however, would indicate that pre-emptive slaughter becomes the more advantageous mode of disease abatement.

To date there are no models of a combined vaccination and slaughter control policy within the literature.

4.13. An Integrated Model

Various models have been proposed for inter-herd transmission of FMD, for intra-herd transmission of FMD, for slaughter control and for vaccinal control (Garner, 1992; Pech and Hone, 1988; Pech and McIlroy, 1990; Woods, 1974). An interesting possibility exists in the integration of both inter- and intra-herd aspects of the disease, to produce a universal model that would be applicable for both slaughter and vaccinal control.

In the development of models, field data is frequently examined retrospectively for epidemiological trends that show repeatable characteristics. A second and equally important objective is to minimise the input data for predictive models, to enhance their future usefulness during the course of an epidemic. Hence, not only can a model with minimal input data be used rapidly, but extensive field data may not always be available.

Field data collated for two of the major FMD epidemics encountered in the UK, demonstrated epidemiological characteristics that were closely aligned to intra-herd transmission. Thus, a number of parameters that can be used for modelling disease transmission at the farm level can also be used for modelling at regional or national level. FDI, POV, r1, and other parameters are equally applicable to outbreak and epidemic simulations for farms, geographical regions or within the national herd. A single spatial grid enables one modelling approach to be used interchangeably, creating scenarios of use to farmers, regional and national veterinary administrators alike (Figures 16, 17, 18). The units of the spatial grid can be input and mapped similarly, whether these be for animals, herds or groups of herds. The fact that various control measures are available at different (spatial) levels, and for both slaughter and vaccinal control, means that an integrated model could be universally applied to FMD-free regions, as well as areas where FMD is endemic.

A third objective of an integrated model would be to list and prioritise control measures, particularly where climatic and epidemic conditions change. This is again important since a variety of control measures are available for different environments and for different control policies.

Key concept 16: **A forth and perhaps the most significant objective of an integrated model, would be the inclusion of a suitable cost-benefit analysis, examining the economic trade-offs between slaughter of infected herds, pre-emptive slaughter, animal housing measures and availability, use of additional sanitation, herd vaccinations and monitoring of immune status, strategic vaccination, geographic and topographic considerations, and other factors. The optimal economic strategies at farm, regional and national levels are likely to change during the course of an epidemic / outbreak.**

With the expansion of world trade and the scheduled creation of a single European economic market, it may be likely that FMD epidemics will be encountered within the UK in the future. An integrated predictive model for future FMD outbreaks could become a useful tool.

4.14. Integrating Models of Inter- and Intra-Herd Foot-and-Mouth Disease

The majority of epidemiological models for foot-and-mouth disease (FMD) have used climatic conditions to predict the spread of airborne disease over large regional areas, considering the farm as a single unit for disease spread. These inter-herd models may be improved by their integration with appropriate intra-herd models. An example of integrating different modelling styles can be seen for hot, dry environmental conditions where the FMD virus may not achieve extensive distribution via airborne disposal, and contact spread should be incorporated into an inter-herd model. Questions however, are raised as to whether intra-herd factors incorporated into inter-herd models allow more general applicability to different herds and variable conditions. For example, whilst contact spread is applicable to hot, dry environments, can it similarly be modelled within humid, more temperate regions?

4.15. Field Data

Epidemics of Foot-and-Mouth Disease (FMD) have been evident in Great Britain since 1839 (Board of Agriculture and Fisheries Report, 1912), and initiated the commencement of research at the Institute for Animal Health, Pirbright (IAHP) in 1925 (Brooksby, 1986). A number of subsequent outbreaks in the British Isles have been reported (MAP/MAFF Reports 1952-54, 1967, 1968, and others) with corresponding analysis of primary and secondary outbreaks, topographical data, clinical and epidemiological species differences, possible outbreak sources (including airborne virus and avian migration), economic evaluations of slaughter and vaccinal control policies, and general virology of the disease (Brooksby, 1986; Donaldson, 1973; Donaldson et al., 1982; Donaldson, 1986; Hugh-Jones and Wright, 1970; MAF Report, 1952-54; MAFF Report, 1968; Mowat, 1986). Consequently, the expanding volume and variety of knowledge in these fields have become inherently more difficult to monitor. The World Reference Laboratory (WRL) at IAHP holds a unique and growing volume of data from Saudi Arabia, detailing daily outbreak incidence for FMD within large dairy herds - Beal and McCallon (1982) have pointed out that adequate incidence data is frequently difficult to obtain, and the IAHP data was supplemented by comprehensive serological studies. The Saudi herds were monitored for over a decade, forming closed populations of known size and ages. Cohort studies have examined the antibody levels in groups of animals within the herds, following different vaccination regimes. Moreover, outbreak strains have been antigenically and biochemically characterised. The data represented an ideal basis upon which to formulate a model of FMD outbreaks within managed herds (Figure 58).

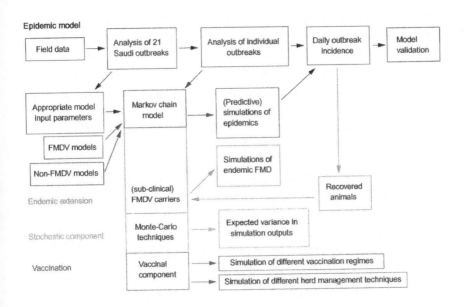

Figure 58. Epidemic model.

4.16. Foot-and-Mouth Disease Virus

Foot-and-mouth disease virus (FMDV) is a member of the Aphthovirus genus of the family Picornaviridae, with seven designated serotypes (O, A, C, SAT 1, SAT 2, SAT3 and Asia 1) and numerous distinct strains within these serotypes. The disease is characterised by fever, with vesicles appearing in the mouth, on the muzzle, feet, teats and udder of affected animals (Blowey and Weaver, 1991). Over seventy species of artiodactyl are susceptible to FMD, including cattle, sheep, goats and pigs. Morbidity within a herd is often high whilst mortality usually only occurs in young animals. FMD is a disease of major economic consequence in that its high transmission rate can cause large production losses, particularly in milk yields. Moreover, as few as 10 infectious units may initiate clinical disease in bovines by the respiratory route.

Few countries have escaped outbreaks of FMD, namely New Zealand, Japan, and some Central American countries (Scott, 1990). However, FMD is absent from the UK, Canada, Australia, USA and many mainland European countries, whilst it is endemic in most of Asia, South American countries and large parts of Africa (Sellers and Daggupaty, 1990). The serotypes O, A and C are prevalent in South America, Europe, Africa and Asia, whilst SAT 1, SAT 2 and SAT 3 serotypes occur in Africa. Asia 1 is only found in Asia.

Diagnosis of FMDV is achieved by identifying virus or viral antigen in samples of vesicle fluid, epithelial fragments, blood or post-mortem tissues (Hamblin et al., 1987). Following a positive result, biochemical and serological techniques are used to identify the genomic/antigenic characteristics of the virus and the outbreak source. Hence an appropriate vaccine can be selected for control (Kitching, 1988; Kitching 1989; Kitching, 1991).

The ability of the FMD virus to transmit to partially-immune and susceptible animals (from affected, mildly-affected and recovered individuals) can be considered in three stages:

    i.   the production and release of virus from an infected animal,
    ii. the survival of FMDV outside the host, and
    iii. the infection of cells in a new host.

The transitions between disease groups that model host infection, encompass all of the stages listed above.

The vaccine against FMD is a dead preparation and vaccinal immunity after administration declines at a well documented rate (Bercan et al., 1969; Mackowiak et al., 1962). For animals that are under 3 years of age and regularly vaccinated, the waning of immunity is proportional to the decline in circulating antibody (Brooksby, 1969; Van Bekkum, 1969; McCullough and Kihm, 1991). Some cattle may not appear to respond to vaccination. This may be for a variety of reasons, such as poor vaccinal efficiency (where less than 100% of the vaccinated animals are protected), excessive time intervals between vaccinations (allowing the antibody titres to wane), or failure to vaccinate some herd animals (due to administrative failure). However, where vaccination is properly managed and monitored, it can keep disease outbreaks to a minimum (Kitching and Knowles, 1994).

The 3 to 6 month old age group is of particular significance in vaccinated herds. Calves receive a protective level of antibody derived from their dams' colostrum and this 'passive' immunity declines during the months after parturition until the calves become susceptible to infection. Susceptibility usually occurs between 3-5 months of age, depending upon the initial level of antibody and the amount and antigenic characteristics of the challenge virus. Passive immunity however, also prevents a calf from responding to vaccination, so that effective vaccination or 'active' immunity can only occur when the antibody level has fallen below an ELISA titre of 1:45. Since these young animals are susceptible to infection at titres above 1:45, then there is a period of weeks in which little protection is offered against a viral challenge. It is essential in an endemic situation to reduce this period to a minimum.

Similarly the 10-18 month age group and pregnant heifers also may from 'at risk' populations. In the latter case, group animals often possess levels of antibody that should adequately provide protection. However, immunosuppression during pregnancy (enabling pre-partal foetal survival) may be a significant factor in pregnant heifers' apparent increased susceptibility to FMD. Multiply vaccinated adult cows are considered to be the best protected group in the herd, although clinical cases of FMD are encountered. The cost of vaccination, and the fact that vaccinated cattle can be a disease threat to susceptible animals (Donaldson and Kitching, 1989) justify the slaughter policy of control used in Europe. Nevertheless vaccinal control may be an effective alternative where slaughter is not economically viable (Chema, 1975; Dijkhuizen, 1989; Thieme, 1982).

4.17. r1 and FMDV Serotypes

In areas where FMD is endemic, vaccination is often insufficient to prevent the reoccurrence of occasional outbreaks, and this can be due to a strain or serotype of FMDV that is not antigenically covered by the vaccine (Kitching et al., 1989).

Kitching (1992) defined r1 to quantify the impact of matching FMD vaccine strains to the virus challenge strain. If matching is less than 100% efficient, then the antibody protection levels necessary for protection will be higher than for a perfect match.

4.18. Waves of Infection

Sanson (1992) as part of the EpiMan software, written for the modelling, monitoring and control of FMD in New Zealand, outlined an intra-herd component based on viral output from infected animals. From three cohorts of infection that spread throughout a herd, the level of viral excretion into the environment could be estimated, and this in turn facilitated predictions as to the size of the aerosol plume threatening neighbouring herds. The waves were evidenced by a differential age of lesions and animals from each wave or cohort were spatially segregated within the farm.

The bottlenecks in disease transmission that would be caused by this spatial segregation were a source for the troughs (or abatement) in incidence required to separate distinct cohorts (Figure 59). Moreover, it is unlikely that incubation period alone could act as a separator between waves of infection: this is because transmission continues whilst those already infected are incubating the disease, creating a continual, smooth rise, peak and fall in incidence (Figure 60) until the susceptible pool or the entire herd is infected. Even an initial lag between the introduction of the infection and the diagnosis of clinical cases may be transparent to monitoring if the source is not removed. For example, where infected foodstuffs or unrestricted affected animals have prolonged exposure to the herd (through nomadic or unmanaged neighbouring livestock) the disease will become firmly established before the initial incubation period expires: hence, the source will remain undetected whilst the first clinical diagnosis in the herd is succeeded by a rising procession of others. Indeed, even the subsequent removal of diagnosed cases may fail to halt the rise in incidence, since the FMD infectious period precedes the appearance of clinical signs (Burrows, 1968), and subclinical infectious animals will remain in the herd until the expiry of the epidemic.

Loss of immunity by recovered animals could also create cohorts, yet again this would be over a two year separation period. Partial vaccination of the herd or the use of ineffective vaccines may likewise induce cohorts. Isolated groups formed through behavioural characteristics may have created the minor waves in outbreak data collected for deer populations in California (Keane, 1926). It could possibly be the case that the same factor is applicable to particularly large, managed herds, such as those in Saudi Arabia, but this is unlikely to be significant for smaller, intensively managed herds.

Waves of infection that occur with age dependent diseases such as measles (Anderson and May, 1985), where the birth rate repeatedly replenishes a spent susceptible pool, are less relevant for FMD outbreaks. This is because the host (or susceptible) abundance described by Hone et al. (1992) for an age-independent disease as contagious as FMD, would require herd populations far greater than those currently managed, before endemic oscillations become evident. Recruitment of new susceptibles would be dependent upon an adequate birth rate, or sufficient numbers of animals with waning immunity to replenish the susceptible pool, and this would require a substantial herd size. Kitching and Salt (1995) have reported endemic oscillations on a large Saudi Arabian farm. However, even this example was pseudo-endemic in that persistence was effected through husbandry practises: as previously mentioned, maternally-derived antibody (MDA) in calves inhibits the formation of vaccinal antibodies. At 5-6 months old, vaccinated calves become susceptible through waning MDA and poor vaccinal response. On the Saudi farm, 6 month old calves were housed next to younger animals and through susceptibility became a source of infection to the 5-month old animals: these in turn incubated the disease, eventually showing clinical signs upon reaching the 6-month old pen.

Indeed, the shortening of the FMD incubation period as the disease progresses (Donaldson, 1987) would tend to enhance an increase in incidence, rather than create troughs (or abatement) to separate cohorts. Thus, as the level of virus increases during an outbreak, animals with higher levels of antibody protection would succumb to infection, and this is also likely to continue the rise in incidence rather than form cohorts.

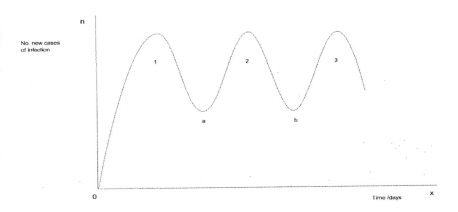

Three cohorts of incidents (labelled 1-3) as outlined by Sansone (1992). Labels a and b mark the troughs that delimit cohorts.

Figure 59. Possible simulation of intra-herd FMD outbreak as outlined by Sanson (1992).

In conclusion, waves of FMD incidence are more probably spatial than temporal. This is further supported by outbreak data from Saudi Arabia (Figures 61 and appendix 62). The stochastic fluctuations that are evident in the herd incidence of Figures 61 and 62, are mirrored in the incidence for segregated age groups (colour coded in the Figures). Ignoring these fluctuations, both total herd incidence and the incidence for segregated pens, demonstrate peaks that match Figure 60. Thus each herd pen (or segregation) can be treated as a distinct sub-model of the overall farm model, and the incidence waves across a farm can be explained by farm segregations.

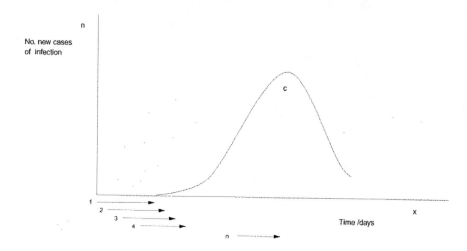

Successive incubation periods (1-n) of equal length for infected animals, ensure a smooth rise in incidence to peak labeled c.

Figure 60. Simulation of intra-herd FMD outbreak as mapped by SIR model.

Where the disease spreads to a new pen and a fresh peak commences (in Figures 61 and 62), the overall herd incidence also increases. Hence, the culmination of several minor peaks from farm pens results in a large overall upturn in incidence. Moreover, some pens are re-infected (Figure 62, day 24) and these also create peaks in herd incidence. Whilst re-infection could create temporal waves, only one of the nine groups in Figures 61 and 62 showed re-infection sufficient to affect herd incidence. In other words, re-infection is not shown to cause incidence waves across the farm. Moreover, although waves created by re-infection could be separated temporally, they would still be a product of spatial segregations on a farm.

Incidentally, the last 46 days of incidence in Figure 62 appear inflated (due to re-scaling for visual clarity), and the apparent peak of days 54-61 is in fact just a continuation from day 53. A consequence of introducing more cohorts than necessary into the intra-herd model (above the number of management segregations in a herd), would be to underestimate the scale of the aerosol plume excreted from the farm. This in turn, could influence the accuracy of the inter-herd modelling, dependent upon the disparity in the mismatch, the scale of the overall viral output from the farm, and the number of farms involved in the modelled outbreak: the reverse would be true for having more management segregations than cohorts in the intra-herd component.

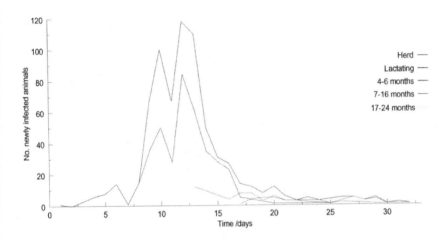

Figure 61. Herd incidence in Al Kharj FMD outbreak (1992).

4.19. Intra-Herd Segregations

Where cohorts of FMD may be evident due to management segregations, they should be built into an intra-herd model as artefacts rather than the epidemiology of the disease – to do otherwise would be to assume that all FMD epidemics exhibit cohorts. This would entail modelling the animal segregations as separate components with respective effective contact rates (determined by FDI), variable immunity titres and other input parameters, and the output data would be similarly compartmentalised. A free-range or wild, undivided herd could be treated as a single group.

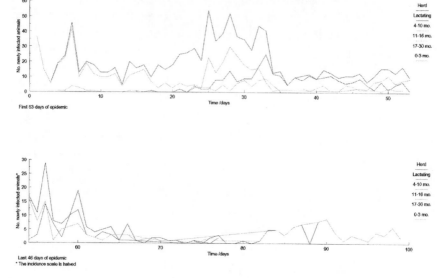

Figure 62. Herd incidence in Nakheel FMD outbreak (1994).

Key concept 17: **Inputting biofactors or other factors into biomodels does not affect model accuracy. The predictive accuracy of a biomodel is dependent upon the biofactor(s) input into it. The poor predictive accuracy of first generation models resulted from the large number of parameters that were required to be guessed quantitatively and from the errors in guessing.**

It is important to note that whilst FMD is an age independent disease and is not restricted to a specific age group, age inherently denotes reproductive status, and reproductive status affects both the level of disease incidence and the severity of clinical signs. The division of an intra-herd model into suitable age groups therefore provides an accurate, simplified framework around which to develop additional model components - typically, these could include a vaccinal programme, variance in challenge (or viral output) and variability in the level of antibody protection (Fox et al., 1971; Yorke et al., 1979). With managed herds, to exclude the option for age group segregations would be dismissing a source of modelling heterogeneity: for example, the EpiMan cohorts (or bottlenecks in incidence discussed above) necessitate a component to accommodate spatial heterogeneity within the model. Kaneene and Miller (1995) have pointed out that using options within models [or optional models] can provide conclusions that might otherwise have been missed.

The case for developing a segregated intra-herd model for FMD is further strengthened by the work of Gibbs (1992) and serological data from Saudi Arabia. Where managed herds are regularly vaccinated and are usually divided into age groups, these age groups exhibit differential levels of vaccinal antibody or susceptibility to infection (Gibbs, 1992). Pregnant heifers for example with reduced immunity, may well be a vulnerable target group for the introduction of disease, whilst very young calves are invariably immune to infection through high levels of passive immunity. Five to six month old calves have little protection through maternally-derived antibody, and some fail to develop protective vaccinal antibody. Discrete model age groups with respective parameters for antibody titre or effective contact rates, would accommodate such differences whilst also modelling the managed structure of the herd.

4.20. Vaccinal Model Components

EpiMan was later adapted to model outbreaks in Europe (at the Institute for Animal Health, 1993), and a vaccinal component was also added. Few intra-herd FMD models have been proposed with a vaccinal component (Cleland et al., 1993). This is probably due to a frequent implementation of the more effective slaughter policy, although Morgan et al. (1984) have pointed out that FMD has been successfully eradicated through vaccination. Carpenter and Thieme (1979) included a vaccinal component in their modelling of FMD economic effects: the modelling was specifically designed for use with South American data where an endemic state was applicable, and was inherently less appropriate for epidemic data or vaccinal control within managed farms.

Hugh-Jones (1981) has proposed a vaccination model for disease epidemics, designed principally to address questions of vaccinal control in rabies. Nevertheless, his derivation of vaccinal immunity through the susceptible fraction vaccinated and the efficacy of the vaccine, provides apt input parameters for a model of managed herds. Indeed, a vaccinal component of an intra-herd model need not be over complex, but ought to contain options for vaccinating different segregated groups on separate days (especially where the herd is sizeable); it should also accommodate the eventuality of highly and less susceptible groups receiving unequal numbers of courses, in order to maximize the efficiency of the vaccination programme. More importantly, the vaccinal programme should be omissible and permit the accurate modelling of an unvaccinated herd.

4.21. Sensitivity Analysis

Omitting insignificant components from simulation models enhances the clarity of the modelling as well as the usability and efficiency of any software employed. For example, in the adaption of the James-Rossiter model (1989) in Figure 2 clinical cases that are removed from the herd become 'isolated yet still infectious' before entering the absorbing state of 'recovered'. This intermediary status ('isolated but infectious') can be simulated and consequently omitted altogether by reducing the infectious period, from onset of viral output to the end of clinical signs: 'isolated but infectious' in this instance is synonymous with 'not infectious to the herd'. Hence, if infectious animals are isolated from the herd, the infectious period is effectively reduced. Similarly, the partially-immune and mildly-affected groups necessary for vaccination modelling, would be less relevant for unvaccinated herds. A sensitivity analysis to highlight the salient features of an FMD model is therefore a useful facet of the development process.

Ma and Ackerman's SENSEN software (1993) was written to identify the critical parameters of stochastic micropopulation models, and such an approach affords empirical assessment of the factors affecting the course of an epidemic - differentiating them from those that have improbable significance.

The absorbing state of recovered animals in Figure 2 is only absorbing in the medium term. Although recovered animals no not leave their disease group for the duration of the epidemic, two years later they may enter the partially-immune or susceptible states. Model complexity and the critical components of any model may therefore change, particularly where simulations are extended to accommodate additional features of an epidemic.

4.22. Carrier Status

An important factor in FMD epidemiology that has unclear potential for modelling, is the carrier status. FMD carriers in the form of recovered animals probably represent the most likely source of FMD persistence. Teclaw (1979) has pointed out that the highly infectious nature of FMD makes the disease less applicable to a double-binomial model, in the sense that persistence through adequate host (or susceptible) abundance is improbable. In other words endemic FMD is unlikely, via constant renewal and re-infection of uninfected herd pools; this is because renewal through birth for example, may never keep apace with the high rate of FMD transmission. Hurd et al. (1993) have described the double-binomial model mentioned by Teclaw. They outline the Reed-Frost bimodal waves that occur, in the number of total cases per epidemic for infectious diseases. The first peak or wave equates to the disease epidemic (delimited by fade-out from the initial levels of incidence). The second peak represents persistence. The fact that bimodal waves are not simply applicable to FMD heightens the importance of inter-epidemic and inter-herd carriers as modes of FMD persistence.

A difficulty in modelling carrier status is that carriers excrete low and often intermittent levels of virus (Donaldson and Kitching, 1989). Virus has been recovered from cattle up to 2.5 years after infection (Hedger, 1970), although experimentally infected animals fail to excrete virus beyond 15 months (Burrows, 1966): there is also a progressive decline in viral excretion during the carrier period (Rossi et al., 1988). Cattle that recover from clinical FMD and even vaccinated cattle that have had contact with the virus and have resisted clinical disease, often develop into carrier animals. Brooksby (1968) and Radostits et al. (1994) have suggested that carrier animals (produced through vaccination) provide a medium for the mutation of existing viral strains. Hugh-Jones (1986) has proposed a model for antigenic drift, and Domingo et al. (1985) report extreme genome heterogeneity for FMD in tissue culture. Emerging quasi-species could perhaps be modelled using discrete or heightened ECRs where appropriate, although the field evidence for carrier infection of susceptibles is currently circumstantial (Kitching, 1992). Hence, whilst the mechanisms for FMD persistence have been investigated substantially (Salt, 1993), they have not to date been clearly elucidated (Woodbury, 1995). Vaccination prior to FMD exposure does not prevent the establishment of the carrier state, and this places carrier animals into relevance for both vaccinated and unvaccinated herds (Kitching 1992).

4.23. Systems Modelling

Future models of intra-herd FMD may well become a composite of components and methodologies apparent in preceding examples, and increasingly in the mode of 'systems modelling' as classified by Hurd and Kaneene (1993). For example, a model of intra-herd FMD could be based both upon the herd immunity concepts of Cleland et al. (1993) and the challenge levels outlined by Sanson (1992). Systems modelling remains creatively open in its fundamental approach, with an overall objective to glean appropriate characteristics from various models and techniques. FMD epidemiology is inherently suited to micropopulation simulation as defined by Anderson and May (1991), although the rudiments of models from non-FMD micropopulation diseases may have relevance for intra-herd FMD. Thus, the Monte-Carlo stocasticism and partially-immune/mildly-affected states of the Rinderpest model (James and Rossiter, 1989) can also be appropriate for an intra-herd FMD model. Miller (1976) has pointed out that there may be many models proposed for the same disease, each with a unique and appropriate contribution to make. For example Carpenter (1988) has outlined a useful application of spreadsheets to modelling as an alternative to the traditional programming approach.

Baldock (1992), and others have described and used case examples to illustrate a number of current modelling styles, with discussions of the methodologies employed and the problems they addressed. A variety of these and numerous other inter/intra-herdal and non-FMD models have been examined for their applicability to FMD within managed herds (Anderson, 1992; Capasso, 1993; Carpenter, 1988; Carpenter and Thieme, 1979; Coyne et al., 1989; De Jong and Dickmann,1992; Fenner et al., 1987; Hugh-Jones et al., 1975; Morris, 1976; Morris and Anderson, 1976; Morris 1991; Peterson et al., 1993; Rubinstein and Beltran, 1975; Smith and Grenfell, 1990; Sorensen et al., 1995).

Section C: Disease Control

Key concept 18: **Macro epidemiological factors such as subclinical disease can assist administrators to decide *where* and *when* to implement disease control measures. Micro epidemiological factors can assist administrators *how* to implement the control measures.**

Macro epidemiological factors include the successful use of historic disease control measures, and *where* disease control measures are implemented largely depends upon the disease status of a given region. Hence [the level and severity of] control measures have historically been implemented according to the generality:

endemic regions > semi-endemic regions > disease-free regions.

Macro epidemiological measures can assist administrators to determine *when* control measures should be implemented. Typically such decisions for administrators are based upon the economical merits of alternative disease control strategies. For example, an assessment of whether to implement a regional vaccination programme could be approached via the following economic equation (Hutber et al., 2005):

Economic viability = [(prevalence without vaccination x unit compensation costs for culling) + export losses for epidemic duration + export losses during post epidemic ban due to culling] − [cost of targeted vaccinations + cost of lost exports during ban due to vaccination]

The temporal ban lengths on product exports from an epidemic region [that subsequently might carry pathogenic material to other susceptible pools] will vary according to the notifiable disease in question and its relevant epidemiology.

The levels of prevalence and outbreak duration [cited in the above equation] can be quantified through measurement of the relevant biofactors.

Micro epidemiological factors are geographically local and specific in terms of indicating *how* disease control measures should be implemented.

For example, modelling spatial dimensions permits the variant topography of any given location or region to be considered, and therefore enables management techniques to be simulated as preventive measures. Hence, vulnerable age or reproductive population groups can be protected from areas of possible infection source by locating them away from incoming vehicles, new individuals or livestock, etc. Individuals with low susceptibility (perhaps offspring of vaccinated dams with maternally-derived antibodies) could be placed strategically at bottleneck locations in the site topography, since this may impede or halt transmission. Additional preventive measures can be simulated, such as accuracy in matching a vaccine to the outbreak strain, the effects of environmental stress, significance of rising challenge during an outbreak or epidemic, the identification and isolation of subclinically infected individuals, zero grazing [for animals] during critical periods of epidemiological significance, the use of spatial barriers, the use of buildings as physical barriers against aerosol transmission, and so forth.

Using biomodels to simulate the impact of different micro epidemiological factors (such as the disease control measures outlined in the paragraph above), provides administrators with an insight into how each disease control measure will impact a given epidemic [or outbreak] in terms of incidence, prevalence and duration: incidence, prevalence and duration will be quantified as output values from the respective biomodel simulations.

Chapter 5

Future Models

The application of biomodelling to the control and prevention of disease is an iterative process. It should not only incorporate the identification of biofactors and their integration into biomodelling algorithms but the process also requires a validation of any given model.

Key concept 19: **There is no substitute in terms of model validation for pre-outbreak or pre-epidemic incidence, prevalence and duration predictions, with a subsequent comparison of these predictions against the generated post-outbreak or post-epidemic field data. Retrospective analysis alone is not a complete validation of any model, since model components and inputs can be suitably adjusted to achieve model simulation mirroring of the post-outbreak or post-epidemic field data.**

Epidemiological models can be used specifically to investigate alternative modes of disease control: for example, whether a slaughter or vaccination policy is economically appropriate to control a regional epidemic of FMD, or to investigate the effects of reducing the age of Rubella immunisation for pre-pubertal girls.

Intra-cellular infectious diseases are equally suited to biomodelling as extra-cellular parasitic infections, both in the fields of human and veterinary medicine. Moreoever, biomodels may be constructed to simulate the aetiology in terms of spatial dimensions as well as temporally, and to accommodate the increasingly divergent nature of epidemiology in terms of emerging quasi-species. Failures in epidemiological control strategies can be addressed retrospectively, for example to investigate the spread of bovine spongiform encephalopathy in the UK, and implications for transmission to humans in the form of new variant Creutzfeldt-Jakob disease.

The benefit of the accurate predictive capabilities demonstrated by biofactors and biomodels, becomes significant when they are applied to the most economically important global diseases and the diseases that hold the greatest humanitarian significance.

Biofactors such as FDI and FFI measure subclinical disease at the start of an outbreak or epidemic, and are therefore available when the number of epidemic foci or infected segregations is low and man-power resources are not at a premium.

5.1. Disease Ratios

Key concept 20: **Many infectious diseases demonstrate subclinical disease. However, the usefulness of subclinical disease as a biofactor to model any given disease is dependent upon the disease ratio (DR), where DR is the ratio of subclinical disease to the acute disease form.**

Acute disease and subclinical disease show disparate clinical signs, and the level of subclinical disease is directly measured through the biofactors FDI and FFI. Acute disease is measured by the number of individuals showing severe clinical signs. Infectious diseases with low levels of subclinical disease cannot use FDI or FFI as predictive biofactors.

Hence, the disease ratio (DR) between individuals showing mild clinical signs (which follow on from subclinical disease) and acute clinical signs, is optimally 1:1. When a disease ratio is 1:1, the predictive capabilities of a biomodel are optimally balanced alongside the disease control capabilities of the biomodel. Hence a biomodel holding a DR value of 1, permits optimal predictions to be made about the spread of a disease, whilst at the same time the disease demonstrates epidemiological characteristics that permit a rapid control of the spread.

The disease ratio (DR) of subclinical to acute forms is equally relevant for diseases with short incubation periods and rapid transmission rates (such as FMD), as it is for a disease with a longer incubation period and a slower transmission rate (such as Tuberculosis). The DR for FMD has been measured at 1:1, whilst the DR for TB has been measured at 3:1.

All diseases with a measurable DR can benefit from the application of biomodels. Biomodels can be used to answer relevant questions such as the possible success of a badger cull in reducing the UK TB prevalence ie. it is currently 600% higher than other EU countries and grew by 20% over the past decade.

5.2. Targeted Control Measures

Targeting control measures remains important during epidemics when man-power resources become scarce. Micro epidemiological factors form an important role in determining how to implement disease control measures and how to incorporate them into a regional contingency plan for future epidemics.

Some factors are simplistic. Hence, protecting susceptible pools is not only important in terms of abating disease spread, but it remains equally relevant to protect groups of individuals that excrete high levels of pathogen and potentially can become a source of rapid disease spread: for this reason, porcine hosts that contract FMD should be culled [within geographical regions that usually hold disease-free status]. Conversely, cattle turned out to spring pasture with sheep, and epidemic foci where the disease incidence is high, represent situations where a vaccination programme should be considered.

Moreover, high levels of FDI or FFI indicate the need to implement both spatially and temporally extensive control measures, counteracting the widespread occult spread of subclinical disease that will have occurred prior to diagnosis. Conversely, low levels of FDI or FFI indicate that the acute disease forms have not transmitted infection occultly prior to diagnosis, and rapid disease control is likely to abate future transmission. There is however, less urgency for extensive serological surveillance in order to identify extended regions of subclinical infection.

Other micro epidemiological factors are counter-intuitive, and as such it remains important to consider the local epidemiology for any given disease when formulating a contingency plan for future epidemics.

Key concept 21: **Contingency plans should not be heavily biased towards the findings of any given epidemiological model. However, they should be biased towards the epidemiology.**

For example, despite the culling of livestock from infected premises (IP) during the 2001 UK FMD epidemic, it remained within the interests of the farming community to reduce viral excretion from any given IP: this minimised the risk of disease spread to neighbouring (contiguous) premises (CPs), or to dangerous contact (DC) farms. Significantly, only 13 of the 187 outbreaks recorded by VLA Starcross for South-West England (the second largest focus during the 2001 UK epidemic) were detected by veterinary surveillance: the majority (153) were reported by farmers, indicating that the farming community would continue with control measures despite personal losses. Such local knowledge in terms of the epidemiology within a region becomes vital for the formation of future contingency plans, and supersedes any conflicting findings from epidemiological modelling.

5.3. Disease Specific Measures

Not only will any given geographical region demonstrate specific epidemiological characteristics that require examination during the formulation of future contingency planning, but also any given disease will retain a number of disease specific epidemiological characteristics that will afford specific effective control measures.

For example, the following biosecurity and farm management techniques that have been found to abate FMD transmission (Hutber and Kitching, 2000), and can be implemented preventively or as a means of regional control. These include:

i.   Creation of spatial bottlenecks between livestock pens or blocks of pens (by strategically removing or relocating animals);
ii. Use of unused housing for livestock;
iii. Re-use of animal housing to prioritise the protection of species shedding most virus (pigs > cattle > sheep although pigs are less susceptible to the aerosol route than via contact spread);
iv. Re-use of animal housing to prioritise the protection of more vulnerable age groups within bovine herds (in-calf heifers> 4-16 month young stock> 1st/2nd lactation cattle > $3^{rd}/4^{th}/5^{th}$ lactation cattle> 0-3 month calves> dry cows);
v.   Removal of animal access to the back of buildings, where air flow carries viral plumes;
vi. Use of physical or natural barriers between livestock and the direction of known IPs;

vii. Movement of livestock to farm areas at the greatest distance from the direction of known IPs.

5.4. Local and Geographic Heterogeneity

It remains important to model the heterogeneity of the local outbreak environment as well as the geographic epidemic environment. Hence in Figures 16, 17 and 18 the local topography (of a managed livestock site) is mapped via data input and the spatial relationship between segregated (but in-contact) populations can be varied by the software operator.

Premises heterogeneity remains an integral component of accurate modelling, being evident in terms of the differing species that are modelled, variance in reproductive status of individuals or individuals' age, peculiarities for site topography impacted by spatial and physical barriers, and welfare considerations such as host movement restrictions during outbreaks or epidemics ie. travel restrictions for individuals suspected of carrying Ebola infection, or ewes requiring passage across public roads to access lambing enclosures. Heterogeneity thus ensures that the modelling of each local site (as a potential IP) becomes necessary, in order to monitor the level of viral excretion and disease transmission to other susceptible pools.

Clearly in the absence of temporal, economic or man-power resources, detailed local modelling becomes impracticable, and biofactors remain the primary source of epidemiological predictions for disease control purposes.

5.5. Retrospective Analysis

During periods of epidemic or outbreak crisis, accurate predictions afforded by biofactors and biomodels become invaluable. However, during long periods of disease abatement, when epidemics and outbreaks are not encountered, it becomes possible to undertake retrospective analysis of historic epidemics and outbreaks. Such an analysis can highlight insights into the failures of previous disease control measures, and allow administrators the opportunity to refine future contingency plans.

For example, the vaccination programmes implemented across large dairy herds in Saudi Arabia [where the disease was endemic] were failing to provide adequate livestock protection for the following reasons:

i.   Less than 100% efficiency of the vaccines in primary vaccinations with low rl values;
ii. Failure to re-vaccinate before average population titres fell below protection;
iii. Failure to re-vaccinate susceptible individuals (resultant from i) before a challenge was mounted;
iv. Failure to isolate the source of infection (particularly within vulnerable groups) from the susceptible pool;
v.   An insufficient interval between secondary vaccination and challenge, curtailing full protection from vaccinal boost;
vi. Failure to control outbreaks before an increase in challenge level (caused by increasing numbers of infected individuals excreting pathogen) reduced vaccinal efficiency.

There was a distinction between (ii) and (iii) above in that the former addressed the need to maintain an administration interval within the period of vaccine durability, whilst the latter was concerned with reducing the number of unprotected individuals left immediately after vaccination.

5.6. Prophylactic Control Measures

In recognition of the vaccination failures listed above, a number of corrective control measures were incorporated into future contingency plans. Namely:

1. Populations were prophylactically vaccinated at regular intervals, with each interval lasting no longer than 2.5 months;
2. Vaccines with the highest possible efficacy were used, in order to decrease the number of unprotected individuals when the population might be challenged in the future;
3. All clinically infected individuals were isolated from the susceptible pool immediately after diagnosis, and any individuals that were suspected of incubating the disease were similarly isolated;
4. The entire population was blanket vaccinated as soon as possible after the initial diagnosis of disease within the susceptible pool.

Further review considerations were also relevant following the changes to the contingency planning, and these included the following:

There was a possibility that desensitisation to vaccine could result from a decrease in the vaccination interval. Hence a solution to the Saudi vaccine failure might not have been approachable through factors (ii) and (iii) above. Moreover, a 75-day interval appeared to have been 81%-98% successful, such that the benefits of reducing the vaccinal interval below 75 days might not outweigh the disadvantages. An improvement in factor (i) above would obviously have a significant impact upon the reduction of disease incidence. Since vaccination of a population is usually accomplished within 1-2 days of initial disease diagnosis, there was little probability of reducing the interval in (v). One alternative to addressing factors (ii) and (iii) via a shortening of the vaccinal interval, was to isolate infected individuals from the rest of the population at diagnosis. This measure effectively protected the population by eliminating the source of infection. However, a difficulty with the removal of infectious individuals was diagnosing individuals that were incubating the disease, since the pathogen was excreted before the appearance of clinical signs.

The presence of incubating individuals was detectable by a high number of disease cases on the first day of the outbreak (perhaps >3). For example, subclinical, mildly-affected source individuals excreting virus could spread the disease and create incubating individuals before being diagnosed. When clinical signs become evident on day one of the outbreak, there would be a number of former incubating individuals that showed signs together. However, source individuals with acute signs of the disease could be diagnosed more rapidly, and at the time of diagnosis (on the first day of the outbreak) were less likely to have infected a large number of early incubator individuals.

For outbreaks that may showed a high likelihood of early incubator individuals, disease transmission was impeded by isolating entire infected segregations from the susceptible population; this removed both the infected and incubator individuals from the susceptible pool. Moreover where successful, the isolation of all infective sources from the susceptible pool achieved an early control of local spread, and offered a solution to observation (vi) above. However, there was no field evidence to verify that the removal of entire infected pens significantly impeded inter-segregation transmission.

Hence, it can be seen from the above considerations that the micro epidemiological factors for any given region remain inseparable from the disease control contingency planning.

5.7. Risk Analysis

Whereas cost-benefit analyses examine the economics of different approaches to disease control and produce analytical equations [such as the one for vaccination viability cited above], risk analyses investigate the possible outcomes for predicted scenarios and address the impact of those possibilities.

An interesting possibility in terms of the use of prophylactic vaccination as a control measure is the question of whether to cull livestock post-vaccination. Clearly the question of culling is unique to the veterinary industry but it arises due to the possibility of carrier individuals occurring post-vaccination. Consequently a ban is placed upon the international export of agricultural products for countries encountering epidemics, where disease transmission remains possible via exported agricultural products during the period of the ban.

Vaccination to live during the 2001 FMD epidemic would have incurred a 12-month export ban for UK agricultural products. The epidemic lasted 8 months, and where this was added to the 3-month post-epidemic export ban, the overall export loss was similar to the one for vaccination. If an epidemic was to last as long, or longer than an export ban for vaccination (since the ban length was subsequently reduced), it would become useful to engage the advantages of vaccination (ie. rapid administration, decrease in viral excretion from IPs, preservation of livestock, reduced requirement for limited manpower resources, etc.). If the epidemic was significantly shorter than the ban length, it could become more economically advantageous not to vaccinate. Knowledge of the likely prevalence and duration of an epidemic and its foci can be determined from FDl and FFl. In turn, it becomes possible to determine whether vaccination to live is an economic viability for future epidemics.

5.8. Economic Consequences

Amongst animal populations, livestock diseases reduce productivity (in terms of meat, milk, wool, etc.) and economic farming margins can become negative due to widespread disease. For human populations, industrial output, services, travel, etc. are all affected by widespread disease. Each of the newsworthy epidemics in recent decades (BSE, Foot-and-Mouth Disease, SARS, Avian Flu, Swine Flu, Tuberculosis, etc.) has carried significant economic consequences that have impacted, or held the potential to impact national economies.

5.9. Scaled Biofactors

At the local level steps can be taken to control disease and to reduce the level of pathogenic material that diseased individuals, or groups of individuals, excrete into the environment (Hutber and Kitching, 2000). Local disease control is not only focused upon individuals but also upon their ability to spread disease into a wider population around them. Hence, efforts to reduce disease spread at the local level remain worthwhile.

The same principles that apply to local disease control, also apply to the control of disease spread at a regional level: the most significant difference lies in the fact that the modelling is scaled up, both geographically and temporally. For example 'first day incidence' at the local level becomes 'first fortnight incidence' at the regional level, etc. The scaling up of the biofactor does not affect its ability to predict subclinical disease prevalence.

5.10. Tracing Carriers

Vaccination is usually the preferred method of control for infectious diseases, but for some diseases with low environmental challenges (ie. in disease-free countries) or a long incubation period (ie. Tuberculosis), then culling (of animals) or medical treatment (ie. antibiotics, etc.) may become the optimal method of control (Hutber et al., 2010). This is particularly true where the relevant vaccines are less than 100 per cent efficient, or the excessive use of vaccines can create carrier individuals which subsequently allow the disease to persist and reappear (Hutber, 2007).

It is however, the measured level of subclinical disease which can indicate whether carrier individuals are likely to occur - a high level of measured subclinical disease translates into a high likelihood of carriers. The solution to this problem lies in increasing the surveillance zones around foci of subclinical disease, and also to minimise repeated or regular vaccination programmes. It is worth noting that whilst carriers remain a problem for disease-free regions, they are not an issue for endemic or semi-endemic areas. Carriers will be almost irrelevant in regions of endemic disease since the disease challenge will already be high. Hence vaccination is generally, the most effective disease control tool for endemic regions (Hutber et al., 1998). Carriers will also be less relevant for diseases where vaccination remains the only means of disease control.

For some diseases the method of transmission via carrier individuals remains unclear. It is likely that vaccinated populations succumbing to rising pathogen challenge during an advancing outbreak or epidemic succumb to the increased cumulative excretion of pathogen from elevated numbers of infectious individuals. A similar principle appears to apply to the transmission of disease from carrier animals to susceptible individuals (Hutber and Kitching, 2000).

Tracing carrier individuals and their mode of disease transmission will probably become an interesting area of research for the future.

5.11. Biomodels Q&As

A number of questions have been posed relating to the use of biofactors and biomodels for epidemiological simulations. If biofactors and biomodels are to be used within the industry and by disease control administrators, it is useful to address a few of the most commonly posed questions. Brief answers are posted below.

Q1. Do biomodels have a problem, because is it possible to know everything that is required for an accurate prediction of disease spread?
A. This would be a relevant question if the disease spread had not already occurred, but where it has already occurred the task is to observe the biology that has taken place. FDI (first day incidence) and FFI (first fortnight incidence) have highly significant correlations with disease prevalence and can be monitored accurately. This is true for subclinical disease but not for the other form of disease ie. acute disease. Where biomodels are multifaceted, they also accommodate the acute disease. In the same data sets that originally identified FDI, environmental temperature (as a stressor had no correlation with subclinical disease prevalence, yet) did have a good correlation with acute disease prevalence. Hence, by monitoring additional correlations, the predictive accuracy can be increased. Significant biological correlations overcome the need to guess infectious periods, incubation periods or biologically meaningless mathematics. Accurate correlations separately can provide accurate prevalence predictions, and accurate correlations together can provide accurate simulations. In turn, applying different control measures to an

accurate simulation, will show their relative effectiveness, and thereby indicate which to select.

Q2. If a biomodel can simulate what is likely, then what happens when the next epidemic turns out to be unlikely?

The randomness of stochasticism holds little value in simulations, other than to guess the possible likelihood of 'fadeout' following a successful initial challenge against a susceptible pool. When an epidemic has already commenced the question of fadeout becomes immaterial. Hence, it remains important that subclinical disease has already occurred, because variables are not important once the subclinical transmission has taken place and all variables have become historic.

Q3. Clinical signs could be subclinical in a partially immune or healthy susceptible population, but the disease could be acute in a population with a different concurrent infection. How can a disease biomodel be accurate with so many variables?

A. Variables such as concurrent infections, environmental relative humidity or temperature, or disease challenge levels and population immunity levels will all change. None of those matter with subclinical disease because the subclinical disease transmission has already occurred ie. what happens before clinical signs appear is the disease history that is measured by biofactors such as FDI or FFI. FDI and FFI are correlated with prevalence in vaccinated herds as well as in unvaccinated herds, irrespective of this added variable. The section of a population that has succumbed to acute disease rather than subclinical disease can be measured via another correlating factor (such as POV or environmental temperature, etc.). Generally however, the acute disease form is diagnosed early and is therefore controlled effectively with minimal subsequent transmission: hence, prevalence from acute disease is largely irrelevant and would not need to be predicted. The acute disease form needs to be controlled rather than predicted. The same principle applies to the lack of impact of epidemiological heterogeneity upon biofactor predictive accuracy [as outlined in Key Concept 12].

Q4. The level of subclinical disease transmission will vary between different diseases, and underlying conditions in one epidemic may not be relevant for a different epidemic or a different disease. How can a disease biomodel cater for different diseases?

A. Each disease requires its own biomodel, with observed correlations for prevalence according to a biofactor that becomes relevant. The initial correlation with prevalence will be subclinical disease for many infectious diseases. Baylis et al. (1999) identified a biomodel in measuring rainfall and the spread of the midge vector against African Horse Sickness prevalence. Tatem et al. (2003) identified a biomodel for Bluetongue. The route to proving the accuracy of a biomodel (and thereby gain the confidence of disease control administrators) is not to validate a model by retrospective comparisons of simulations against field data, but to use a model to accurately predict the future.

References

Abbey, H. (1976). An examination of the Reed-Frost theory of epidemics. *Human Biology*, *24*, 201-233.

Ahlbom, A. (1993). Biostatistics for epidemiologists. Boca Raton: Lewis, 17-28.

Anderson, R. M. & May, R. M. (1985). Vaccination and herd immunity to infectious diseases. *Nature*, *318*, 323-329.

Anderson, R. M. & May, R. M. (1991). Infectious diseases of humans: dynamics and control. Oxford: Oxford University Press, p.13, 17-18, 19, 20-21, 75, 305-314.

Anderson, R.M. (1992). The concept of herd immunity and the design of community-based immunisation programmes. *Vaccine*, *10*, 928-935.

Bachrach, H. L. (1977). Foot-and-mouth disease virus properties, molecular biology and immunogenicity. In: Beltsville symposia in agricultural research. I. Virology in agriculture, edited by J.A. Romberger. Montclair, N.J.: Allenbeld, Osmun and Co., p.5.

Baylis, M., Meiswinkel, R. & Venter G. J. (1999). A preliminary attempt to use climatic data and satellite imagery to model the abundance and distribution of Culicoides imicola (Diptera: Ceratopognidae) in southern Africa. *Journal of the South African Veterinary Association*, *70*, 80-89.

Beal, V. C. & McCallon, W. R. (1982). The use of mathematical models in animal disease program evaluation. In: *Third Symposium on Veterinary Epidemiology and Economics*, Arlington, Virginia, USA, 6-10 September, 1982. Kansas: Veterinary Medicine Publishing, 400-407.

Bercan, A., Mintui, N., Dohotaru, V. & Tomescu, A. (1969). On the correlation between the sero-neutralisation test on young mice and immunization against foot and mouth disease in crossbred cows. *Bulletin de l'Office International des Epizooties*, *71*, 381-392.

Blowey, R. W. & Weaver, A. D. (1991). *A colour atlas of diseases and disorders of cattle*. London: Wolfe Publishing, 189-190.

Brooksby, J. B. (1968). Variants and immunity: definitions for serological investigation. In: International Symposium on Foot-and-mouth Disease, Lyon, 1967, edited by R.H. Regamey (Symposia Series in Immunobiological Standardization, 8,). Basel: S.Karger, 1-10.

Brooksby, J. B. (1968). Wild animals and the epizootiology of foot-and-mouth disease. In: Disease in free-living wild animals, 1969, edited by A. McDiarmid. The Zoological Society of London, Academic Press, p.4.

Brooksby, J. B. (1969). Some notes on the dose response relationship. Report of the meeting of the Research Group of the Standing Technical Committee for the European Commission for the Control of FMD, Brescia, Italy. Rome: FAO, 32-37.

Brooksby, J. B. (1986). Foot-and-mouth disease: an introduction. *Revue Scientifique et Technique Office International des Bpizooties*, *5*, 257-263.

Burghes, D. N. & Wood, A. D. (1980). Mathematical models in the social, management and life sciences. Chichester: Ellis Horwood Publishers, p.54.

Burrows, R. (1966). Studies on the carrier state of cattle exposed to foot-and-mouth disease virus. *Journal of Hygiene*, *63*, 81-90.

Burrows, R. (1968). Excretion of foot and mouth disease virus prior to development of lesions. *Veterinary Record*, *82*, 387-388.

Capasso, V. (1993). Mathematical structures of epidemic systems (Lecture Notes in Biomathematics No. 97). Berlin: Springer-Verlag.

Carpenter, T. E. & Thieme, A. (1979). A simulation approach to measuring the economic effects of foot and mouth disease in beef and dairy cattle. In: *Proceedings of the Second International Symposium on Veterinary Epidemiology and Economics*, Canberra, 511-516.

Carpenter, T. E. (1988). Stochastic epidemiological modeling using a microcomputer spreadsheet package. *Preventive Veterinary Medicine*, *5*, 159-168.

Chema, S. (1975). Vaccination as a method of foot-and-mouth disease control. An appraisal of the success achieved in Kenya, 1968-1973. *Bulletin de l'Office International Epizooties*, *83*, 195-209.

Cleland, P. C., Baldock, F. C., Gleeson, L. J. & Pornchai, Chamnanpood. (1993). A modelling approach to the investigation of vaccination strategies for foot-and-mouth disease. In: Diagnosis and Epidemiology of

Foot-and-Mouth Disease in Southeast Asia, *Proceedings of an International Workshop held at Lampang*, Thailand, 6-9 September, 1993, pp. 49-53.

Coyne, M. J., Smith, G. & McAllister, F. E. (1989). Mathematical model for the population biology of rabies in racoons in the mid-Atlantic states. *American Journal of Veterinary Research, 50*, 2148-2154.

Curtis, S. E. & Houpt, K. A. (1983). Animal ethology: its emergence in animal science. *Journal of Animal Science, 57*, (2), 234-247.

Dijkhuizen, A. A. (1989). Epidemiological and economic evaluation of foot-and-mouth disease control strategies in the Netherlands. Netherlands *Journal of Agricultural Science, 37*, 1-12.

Domingo, E., Martinez-Salas, E. & E., Sobrino, F. (1985). The quasispecies (extremely heterogenous) nature of viral RNA genome populations: biological relevance - a review. Gene, 1-8.

Donaldson, A. I., Gloster, J., Harvey, L. D. & Deans, D. H. (1982). Use of prediction models to forecast and analyse airborne spread during the foot-and-mouth disease outbreaks in Brittany, Jersey and the Isle of Wight in 1981. *Veterinary Record, 110*, 53-57.

Donaldson, A. I. (1986). Aerobiology of foot-and-mouth disease (FMD): an outline and recent advances. Revue Scientifique et Technique Office International des Epizooties, 5, 315-321. Donaldson, A.I. (1987). Foot-and-mouth disease: the principal features. *Irish Veterinary Journal, 41*, 325-327.

Donaldson, A. I. & Kitching, R. P. (1987). Experimental investigation of the transmission of infection by vaccinated cattle following their exposure to foot-and-mouth disease virus. In: Report of the session of the Research Group of the Standing Technical Committee of the European Commission for the Control of Foot-and-mouth Disease, Lyons, France. Rome: FAO, 59-61.

Donaldson, A. I. & Kitching R. P. (1989). Transmission of foot-and-mouth disease by vaccinated cattle following natural challenge. *Research in Veterinary Science, 46*, 9-14.

Fenner, F., Bachmann, P. A., Gibbs, E. P., Murphy, F. A., Studdert, F. A. & White, D. O. (1984). Computations and data used by epidemiologists. In: Veterinary virology, 2nd edition. London: Academic Press, 266-268.

Fox, J .P., Elveback, L., Scott, W., Gatewood, L. and Ackerman, E. (1971). Herd immunity: Basic concepts and relevance to public health immunization practises. *American Journal of Epidemiology, 94*, 179-189.

Fraser, A. F. (1980). Farm animal behaviour: an introduction to behaviour in the common Farm species, 2nd edition. London: Balliere Tindall, 160-170.

Frenkel, S., Barendregt, L. G., Kloosterman, E. G. & Talman, F. P. (1982). Serological response of calves to aluminium hyroxide gel FMD vaccine with or without saponin. Influence of genetic differences on this response. XVIth Conference of the Foot and Mouth Disease Commission, Paris, 14-17 September, 1982, 211-218.

Garner, M. G. (1992). Modelling foot-and-mouth disease in Australia. In: *Proceedings of the national symposium on foot-and-mouth disease*, 8-10 September, 1992, edited by M.J. Nunn and P.M. Thornber. Canberra: Australian Government Publishing Service, 177-190.

Garner, M. G. & Lack, M. B. (1995). An evaluation of alternate control strategies for foot- and-mouth disease in Australia: a regional approach. *Preventive Veterinary Medicine, 23*, 9-32.

Geering, W. A. & Forman, A. J. (1987). *Foot-and-mouth disease.* In: Animal health in Australia. 9: Exotic diseases. Canberra: Australian Government Publishing Services, 111-117.

Gibbs, N. S. (1992). Foot and mouth disease at a large dairy establishment: serological studies and vaccination programmes. (Unpublished).

Gloster, J., Blackall, R. M., Sellers, R. F. & Donaldson, A. I. (1981). Forecasting the airborne spread of foot-and-mouth disease. *Veterinary Record, 108*, 370-374.

Goel, Y. P. (1989). A note on some epizootiological observations on foot-and-mouth disease outbreak in an organised herd. *Indian Veterinary Medicine Journal, 13*, 127-129.

Hafez, E. S. E. & Schein, H. W. (1969). The Behaviour of Cattle, 2nd edition. London: Balliere Tindall, 235-295.

Hafez, S. M. (1990). Studies on the control of foot-and-mouth disease in Saudi dairy farms: report I. Riyadh: Ministry of Agriculture and Water, and King Abdul-Aziz City for Science and Technology, 22-24.

Hafez, S. M. (1991). Studies on the control of foot-and-mouth disease in Saudi dairy farms: report II. Riyadh: Ministry of Agriculture and Water, and King Abdul-Aziz City for Science and Technology, 29-31.

Hamblin, C., Kitching, R. P., Donaldson, A. I., Crowther, J. R. & Barnett, I. T. R. (1987). Enzyme-linked immunosorbent assay (ELISA) for the detection of antibodies against foot-and-mouth disease virus III. Evaluation of antibodies after infection and vaccination. *Epidemiology and Infection, 99*, 733-44.

Hedger, R. S. (1970). Observations on the carrier state and related antibody titres during an outbreak of foot-and-mouth disease. *Journal of Hygiene, 68*, 53-60.

Hingley, P. J. (1985). Problems in modelling responses of animals to foot-and-mouth disease vaccine, PhD thesis. Reading: Department of Applied Statistics, University of Reading. Institute for Animal Health (1993) Framework 3 Project. Pirbright: Institute for Animal Health.

Hone, J ., Pech, R. & Yip, P. (1992). Estimation of the dynamics and rate of transmission of classical swine fever in wild pigs. *Epidemiology and Infection, 108*, 377-386.

Honhold, N., Taylor, N. M., Mansley, L. M. & Paterson, A. D. (2003). The effect of animal slaughter on infected premises and the intensity of culling on other premises on the rate of spread of foot and mouth disease. In: *Proceedings of the Society for Veterinary Epidemiology and Preventive Medicine*, Warwick, 31st March-2nd April 2003, 183-194.

Hugh-Jones, M. E. & Wright, P. B. (1970). Studies on the 1967-8 foot-and-mouth disease epidemic. The relation of Weather to the spread of disease. *Journal of Hygiene, 68*, 253-271.

Hugh-Jones, M. E., Ellis, P. & Felton, M. R. (1975). An assessment of the eradication of bovine brucellosis in England and Wales (Study no. 19). Reading: Department of Agriculture and Horticulture, University of Reading.

Hugh-Jones, M. E. (1976). A simulation spatial model of the spread of foot and mouth disease through the primary movement of milk. *Journal of Hygiene, 77*, 1-9.

Hugh-Jones, M. E. (1981). A simple vaccination model. *Bulletin de l'Office International des Epizooties, 93*, 1-8.

Hugh-Jones, M. E. (1986). A mathematical model of antigenic drift. *Mathematical Modelling, 7*, 765-775.

Hurd, H. S. & Kaneene, J. B. (1993). The application of simulation models and systems analysis in epidemiology: a review. *Preventive Veterinary Medicine, 15*, 81-99.

Hurd, H. S., Kaneene, J. B. & Lloyd, J. W. (1993). A stochastic distributed-delay model of disease processes in dynamic populations. *Preventive Veterinary Medicine, 16*, 21-29.

Hutber, A. M. & Kitching, R. P. (1996). The use of vector transition in the modelling of intra-population foot-and-mouth disease. *Environmental and Ecological Statistics, 3*, 245-255.

Hutber, A. M. (1997). Modelling the spread and maintenance of foot-and-mouth disease in a dairy population. PhD thesis. Hertford: The Business School, University of Hertfordshire, 1997.

Hutber, M., Kitching, R. P. & Conway, D. A. (1998). Control of foot-and-mouth disease through vaccination and the isolation of infected animals. *Tropical Animal Health and Production, 30* (4), 217-227.

Hutber, A. M., Kitching, R. P. & Conway, D. A. (1999). Predicting the level of population infection for outbreaks of foot-and-mouth disease in vaccinated populations. *Epidemiology and Infection, 122,* 539-544.

Hutber, A. M. & Kitching, R. P. (2000). The role of management segregations in controlling foot-and-mouth disease. *Tropical Individual Health and Production, 32,* 285-294.

Hutber, M. (2002). Modelling epidemics of foot-and-mouth disease. DVM thesis, Kosice: University of Veterinary Medicine, Slovakia.

Hutber, M., Kitching, R. P. & Pilipcinec, E. (2005). Predictions for the timing and use of culling or vaccination during a foot-and-mouth disease epidemic. *Research in Veterinary Science, 81* (1), 31-36.

Hutber, M. (2006). Learnings from the UK. Bioterrorist-induced foot-and-mouth disease as a complex system problem workshop. CSIRO, 22nd-23rd February, 2006, Geelong, Australia.

Hutber, M. (2007). Guest Editorial: The use of vaccines to control disease is not a simple matter. *The Veterinary Journal, 173,* 480-481.

Hutber, M., Kitching, R. P., Fishwick, J. & Bires, J. (2010). Foot-and-mouth disease: the question of implementing vaccinal control during an epidemic. *The Veterinary Journal, 188* (1), 18-23.

Hutber, M. , Pilipcinec, E. & Bires, J. (2014). Foot-and-mouth disease virus. Manual of Security Sensitive Microbes and Toxins, edited by Dongyou Liu. CRC Press. Chapter 57.

James, A. D. & Rossiter, P. B. (1989). An epidemiological model of rinderpest. 1. Description of the model. *Tropical Animal Production, 21,* 59-68.

Jong de, M. C. M. (1995). Mathematical modelling in veterinary epidemiology: why model building is important. *Preventive Veterinary Medicine, 25,* 183-193.

Jong de, M. C. M. & Diekmann, O. (1992). A method to calculate - for computer-simulated infections - the threshold value, Ro, that predicts Whether or not the infection will spread. *Preventive Veterinary Medicine, 12,* 269-285.

Kaneene, J. B. & Miller, R. (1995). Risk factors for metritis in Michigan dairy cattle using herd- and cow-based modelling approaches. *Preventive Veterinary Medicine*, *23*, 183-200.

Keane, C. (1926). The epizootic of foot and mouth disease in California, February 17, 1924 to June 10, 1926 (Special Publication No. 65). Department of Agriculture, State of California.

Kitching, R. P. (1988). ELISA for selection of foot-and-mouth disease vaccines. Report of the session of the Research Group of the Standing Technical Committee for the European Commission for the Control of F MD, Prague, Czechoslovakia, 20-23 September, 1988, 75-78.

Kitching R. P., Knowles, N. J., Samuel, A. R. & Donaldson, A. I. (1989). Development of foot-and-mouth disease virus strain characterisation - a review. *Tropical Animal Health and Prod*, 1989, *21*, 153- 166.

Kitching, R. P. (1991). Recent advances in the diagnosis of FMD. In: OIE-FAVA Symposium on the Control of Major Livestock Disease in Asia, Pattaya (Thailand), 8-9 November, 1990.

Kitching, R.P. (1992). The excretion of foot-and-mouth disease virus by vaccinated animals. *State Veterinary Journal*, *2*, (3), 7-11.

Kitching, R. P. (1992). The application of biotechnology to the control of foot and mouth disease virus. *British Veterinary Journal*, *148*, 375-388.

Kitching, R. P. (1992). Foot-and-mouth disease. In: Bovine medicine: diseases and husbandry of cattle, edited by A.H. Andrews et al. Oxford: Blackwell Scientific, 537-543.

Kitching, R. P. & Knowles, N. J. (1994). The molecular epidemiology of foot-and-mouth disease. Proceedings of the international symposium on virus-cell interaction: cellular and molecular responses, 22-24th November, 1993. Edited by C.Nataraj an et al. Bangalore: Indian Veterinary Research Institute, 23-27.

Kitching, R. P. (1995). The epidemiology of foot-and-mouth disease and capripox in the Middle East. In: Regional seminar on the application of biotechnology in animal health, Cairo, Egypt, 4-7 December, 1995, 1. Cairo: FAO Regional Office for the Near East, p.1-8.

Kitching, R. P. & Salt, J. (1995). The interference of maternally-derived antibody with active immunization of farm animals against foot-and-mouth disease. *British Veterinary Journal*, *151*, 379-389.

Kitching, R. P. & Hughes, G. J. (2002). Clinical variation in foot and mouth disease: sheep and goats. Revue Scientifique et Technique, *Office International des Epizooties*, *21*, 505-512.

Kitching, R. P., Hutber, M. & Thrusfield, M.V. (2004). A review of foot-and-mouth disease with special consideration for the clinical and epidemiological factors relevant to predictive modelling of the disease. *The Veterinary Journal, 169* (2), 197-209.

Mackowiak, C., Lang, R., Fontaine, 1., Camand, R. & Petermami, H.G. (1962). Relationship between neutralizing antibody titre and protection in animals immunized against FMD. *Annales de l'Institut Pasteur, 103*, 252-261.

McCullough, K. C. & Kihm, U. (1991). The immunology of foot-and-mouth disease. In: OIE-FAVA Symposium on the Control of Major Livestock Diseases in Asia, Pattaya (Thailand), 8-9 November 1990. Paris: Office International des Epizooties, 136-147.

Metz, J. H. M. & Wierenga, H. K. (1986). Behavioural criteria for the design of housing systems for cattle. In: Cattle housing systems, lameness and behaviour, edited by H. Wierenga and D. Peterse. The Hague: Martinus Nijhoff, 14-25.

Miller, W. M. (1976). A state-transition model of epidemic foot and mouth disease. In: Ellis, P.R., Shaw, A.P.M., Stephens, A.J., (Eds.), New Techniques in Veterinary Epidemiology and Economics, *Proceedings of a Symposium, Reading*, 12-17 July 1976, 56-60.

Morgan, D. O., Robertson, B. H., Moore, D. M., Timpone, C. A. & McKercher, P. D. (1984). Aphthoviruses: control of foot-and-mouth disease with genetic engineering vaccines. In: *Control of virus diseases*, edited by E. Kurstak and R.G.Marusyk. New York:. Marcel Dekker, 135-136.

Morris, R. S. (1976). The use of computer modelling in epidemiological and economic studies of animal disease, PhD Thesis. Reading: Reading University.

Morris, R. S. & Anderson, G. A. (1976). Preliminary description of a computer simulation model of foot and mouth disease. In: New techniques in veterinary epidemiology and economics, proceedings of a symposium, edited by P.R. Ellis, A.P.M. Shaw and A.J. Stephens. Reading: Reading University, p.74.

Morris, R. S. (1991). User's guide to Exotica, a computer model of a regional outbreak of a highly contagious animal disease. Massey: Massey University.

Moutou, F. & Durand, B. (1994). Modelling the spread of foot-and-mouth disease virus. In: International Symposium on Ecopathology and

Individual Health Management, Clermont-Ferrand, 18-20 October, 1993. *Veterinary Research*, *25*, 279-285.

Mowat, G.N. (1986). Epidemiology of foot-and-mouth disease in Europe. *Revue Scientifique et Technique Office International des Epizooties*, *5*, 271-277.

O'Connell, J., Giller, P. S. & Meaney, W. (1989). A comparison of dairy cattle behaviourpatterns at pasture and during confinement. *Irish Journal of Agricultural Research*, *28*, 65-72.

Ondrasovic, M., Ondrasovicova, O., Vargova, M. & Sokol, J. (1994). Animal Hygiene, University of Veterinary Medicine, Kosice, Slovakia.

Pech, R. P. & Mcllroy, J. C. (1990). A model of the velocity of advance of foot and mouth disease in feral pigs. *Journal of Applied Ecology*, *27*, 635-650.

Peterson, D., Gatewood, L., Zhuo, Z., Yang, J., Seaholm, S. & Ackerman, E. (1993). Simulation of stochastic micropopulation models - II. Vespers: epidemiological model implementations for spread of viral infections. *Computers in Biology and Medicine*, *23*, (3), 199-213.

Power, A. P. and Harris, S. A. (1973). A cost benefit evaluation of alternative control policies for foot-and-mouth disease in Great Britain. *Journal of Agricultural Economics*, *14*, (3), 573-597.

Radostits, O. M., Blood, D. C. & Gay, C. C. (1994). Veterinary medicine: a textbook of the diseases of cattle, sheep, pigs, goats and horses. London: Balliere Tindall, p.972.

Robinson, R. A., Wickstrom, S. & Linck, J. (1993). Computer-based problem-solving exercises in veterinary epidemiology. *Preventive Veterinary Medicine*, *16*, 57-58.

Rossi, M. S., Sadir, A. M., Schudel, A. A. & Palma, E. L. (1988). Detection of FMDV with DNA probes in bovine esophageal-pharyngeal fluid. *Archives of Virology*, *2*, 67-74.

Rubenstein, E. M. De & Beltran, L. E. (1975). Economic losses from F MD: a case study on a pig farm in Colombia. *Tropical Animal Health and Production*, *7*, 149-151.

Rweyemamu, M. M., Pay, T. W. F. & Simms, M. J. (1982). The control of foot-and-mouth disease by vaccination. *Veterinary Annual*, *22*, 63-80.

Salt, J. S. (1993). The carrier state in foot-and-mouth disease, an immunological review. *British Veterinary Journal*, *149*, 207-223.

Sanson, R. L. (1992). The development of a decision support system for an animal disease emergency, PhD Thesis. Massey: Massey University.

Sanson, R. L., Morris, R. S. & Stern, M. W. (1999). EpiMAN-FMD a decision support system for managing epidemics of vesicular disease. Revue Scientifique et Technique, *Office International des Epizooties, 18,* 593-605.

Schermbrucker, C. G. (1989). Foot-and-mouth disease: an analysis of situation in Saudi Arabia, April 1989. Pirbright: Coopers Animal Health Ltd., FMD Laboratory.

Searle, S. R. & Hausman, W. H. (1970). Markov chains. In: Matrix algebra for business and economics. New York: Wiley-Interscience, 193-212.

Sellers, R. F. & Forman, A. J. (1973). The Hampshire epidemic of foot-and-mouth disease, 1967. *Journal of Hygiene, 71,* 15-34.

Scott, G. R. (1990). Diseases caused by viruses. In: *Animal diseases in the tropics,* edited by M. Sewell and D. Brocklesby. London: Bailliere Tindall, 309-312.

Sellers, R. F. & Daggupaty, S. M. (1990). The epidemic of foot-and-mouth disease in Saskatchewan, Canada, 1951-1952. *Canadian Journal of Veterinary Research, 54,* 457-464.

Smith, G. & Grenfell, B. T. (1990). Population biology of pseudorabies in swine. *American Journal of Veterinary Research, 51,* 148-155.

Sorensen, J .T., Enevoldsen, C. & Houe, H. (1995). A stochastic model for simulation of the economic consequences of bovine virus diarrhoea virus infection in a dairy herd. *Preventive Medicine, 23,* 215-227.

Stricklin, W. R., Graves, H. B. & Wilson, L. L. (1979). Some theoretical and observed relationships of fixed and portable spacing behaviour of animals. *Applied Animal Ethology, 5,* 201.

Tatem, A. J., Baylis, M., Mellor, P. S., Purse, B. V., Capela, R., Pena, I. & Rogers, D. J. (2003). Prediction of bluetongue risk in Europe and North Africa using satellite imagery. *Veterinary Microbiology, 97,* 13-29.

Teclaw, R. F. (1979). Epidemic modelling. In: A study of the potential economic impact of foot and mouth disease in the United States, edited by E.H. McCauley and others. St. Paul:University of Minnesota, p.103-111.

Terpstra, C., Maanen, C. Van & Bekkum, J .G. Van (1990). Endurance of immunity against foot and mouth disease in cattle after three consecutive annual vaccinations. *Research in Veterinary Science, 49,* 236-242.

Thieme, A. (1982). Modelling the cost and benefits of foot and mouth disease control programmes. *In: Proceedings of the Third International Symposium on Veterinary Epidemiology and Economics,* Arlington, 6-10 September, 1982, 384-391.

Tinline, R. R. (1972). A simulation study of 1967-68 FMD epizootic in Great Britain, PhD Thesis. Bristol: Bristol University.

Thrusfield, M. V. (1995). Veterinary epidemiology, 2nd edition. Oxford: Blackwell Science, p.172.

Van Bekkum, J .G. (1973). The carrier state and foot-and-mouth disease. In: Pollard, M. (Ed.), Proceedings of the Second International Conference on Foot-and-Mouth disease. Gustav Stern Foundation Inc., New York, 45-50.

Wierenga, H. K. (1984). The social behaviour of dairy cows: some differences between pasture and cubicle system. In: Proceedings of the International Congress on Applied Ethology – Farm Animals, Kiel, edited by J. Unshelm et al. Kiel: European Association for Animal Production, 135-138.

Wierenga, H. K. & Metz, J. H. M. (1986). Lying behaviour of dairy cows influenced by crowding. In: Ethology of domestic animals, edited by M. Nichelman. Privat, Toulouse: I.E.C., 61-66.

Woodbury, E. L. (1995). A review of the possible mechanisms for the persistence of foot-and-mouth disease virus. *Epidemiology and Infection*, *114*, 1-13.

Woods, A. J. (1974). Epidemic models relating to foot-and-mouth disease, *Biometrics*, *30*, 215-216.

Woolhouse, M., Chase-Topping, M., Haydon, D., Friar, J ., Matthews, L., Hughes, G., Shaw, D., Wilesmith, J., Donaldson, A., Cornell, S., Keeling, M. & Grenfell, B. (2001). Foot-and-mouth disease under control in the UK. *Nature*, *11*, 17th May 2001, 258-259.

Yorke, J. A., Nathanson, N., Pianigiani, G. & Martin J. (1979). Seasonality and the requirements for perpetuation and eradication of viruses in populations. *American Journal of Epidemiology*, *109*, 103-123.

Index

A

abatement, 113, 116, 128, 134, 135, 149
acute infection, 41
adaptability, 6
administrators, vii, viii, 1, 4, 52, 94, 101,
    106, 107, 108, 110, 115, 129, 143, 144,
    149, 154, 156
aetiology, 145
Africa, 131, 156
age, xii, 7, 11, 15, 19, 22, 25, 27, 29, 32, 39,
    43, 44, 48, 68, 69, 71, 72, 90, 98, 113,
    125, 132, 133, 134, 135, 138, 139, 144,
    145, 148, 149
agriculture, 156
aluminium, 159
animal disease, 156, 163, 164
animal slaughter, vii, 160
antibody, xii, 6, 11, 12, 15, 21, 24, 25, 28,
    29, 30, 31, 39, 40, 41, 43, 44, 49, 55, 56,
    57, 58, 60, 68, 75, 76, 80, 88, 89, 94, 96,
    114, 125, 128, 130, 132, 133, 135, 138,
    139, 160, 162, 163
antigen, 132
antigenic drift, 141, 160
APRISM, viii, xi, 3, 6, 102
Asia, 131, 162, 163
assessment, 126, 140, 143, 160
avian, 130

B

bacteria, 7
ban, 127, 143, 144, 152
barriers, 36, 69, 72, 122, 123, 124, 127, 144,
    148, 149
bedding, 113
beef, 157
benefits, 114, 127, 151
bias, 19, 22, 24
biofactors, viii, ix, xi, 101, 102, 103, 104,
    105, 106, 107, 108, 109, 110, 115, 117,
    126, 138, 144, 145, 146, 149, 154, 155
biomodels, viii, ix, 1, 8, 49, 52, 102, 103,
    104, 106, 108, 109, 117, 138, 144, 145,
    146, 147, 149, 154
biotechnology, 162
birth rate, 134
blood, 112, 132
boosters, 114
Brittany, 158
brucellosis, 160

C

Cairo, 162
case examples/study, 142, 164
cattle, 33, 120, 131, 132, 133, 141, 147,
    148, 157, 158, 162, 163, 164, 165